ALL
IN THE
HEAD

All in the Head

DAVID COHEN

Illustrated by
Rowan Barnes-Murphy

KESTREL BOOKS

KESTREL BOOKS
Published by Penguin Books Ltd
Harmondsworth, Middlesex, England

Copyright © 1979 by David Cohen
Illustrations Copyright © 1979 by
Rowan Barnes-Murphy

First published 1979
Published simultaneously in paperback
by Peacock Books

ISBN 0 7226 5422 7
Printed in Great Britain by
Fletcher & Son Ltd, Norwich

For Nicholas and Reuben

Contents

Introduction	9
Vision	13
Smell and Taste	37
Communication	51
Hearing	81
The Way You React	101

Introduction

'Brainless twit!'
'I wish you had brains.'
'Fish is very good for the brain.'

To be brainy means to be clever: to be brainless means to be a fool. It makes it sound as if having a brain were some kind of advantage in life (like being quick). The brainy ones get along better than the rest of us.

But having a brain isn't an advantage; it's a necessity. If you had no brain you wouldn't be able to see, or feel, or hear, or smell or talk. You wouldn't even be able to breathe. In the past, people thought the heart was the most crucial organ in the body. Not so. Medical technology has made it possible to repair the heart or to keep it going artificially. Work is going ahead on a fully artificial heart, but no one can even begin to imagine an artificial brain.

Doctors are now judging whether or not people are dead by the state of their brains. They used to hold a mirror up to the lips of a would-be corpse; if it did not mist over it meant there was no life – no breath meant death. That is changing.

It is easy to record the electrical activity in the brain by placing small and sensitive electrode plates, which are like buttons, on the scalp, and 'listening in' to the brain's electrical hum. When you do this to a person who is awake you get this sort of pattern.

What you are depends on your brain. You are not your brain, but without your brain you could not be, let alone be the person you are now. We are all in the head.

The brain is shaped like a rugby ball and looks like a cauliflower that has been kneaded full of folds. It fits snugly into the skull, and weighs between 1 and 1·5 kilos.

The top part of the brain, the cortex, fits like a cap over the old part of the brain. All mammals have a cortex which controls high-level activities like talking and seeing patterns. The old part of the brain controls more basic functions like breathing and responding to pain, which are common to all living creatures. As you go up the evolutionary ladder from reptiles to dogs to apes to men, the size of the cortex increases. The new brain is divided into two hemispheres. The right hemisphere controls the left side of the body; the left hemisphere, the right.

The brain is connected at the back to the spinal cord, which is like a cable of telephone wires. Through them, the brain receives information from the rest of the body. The spinal cord is also the path through which the brain tells the rest of the body what to do. When you pick up a sugar lump, it is the brain that has sent your hand the message to do so. Without the brain, the body can do very little.

It is easy to forget the brain is the central control for everything we do. Many of our actions are automatic – you don't think about walking or breathing – but the brain controls these actions. However much your legs have practised walking, they cannot do so by themselves; messages from the brain have to set them in motion and monitor them as they go. Even when you are asleep, the brain continues to function – or, at least, parts of it do. No one has solved all the riddles of the brain, which is extremely complicated, but scientists are beginning to understand some of the ways in which parts of it work.

The brain is largely made up of nerve-cells, some of which are very specialized. No one has really counted how many cells there are in the average brain, but estimates vary between ten and twelve thousand million. Some of these cells form pathways that link different parts of the brain. The basic cells are very different shapes and sizes, ranging from one thousandth of a millimetre to a few centimetres in length. The brain is also full of fibres that link various parts of it. The cells and fibres make up what is known as grey matter and white matter. Inside the

BRAIN WAVES

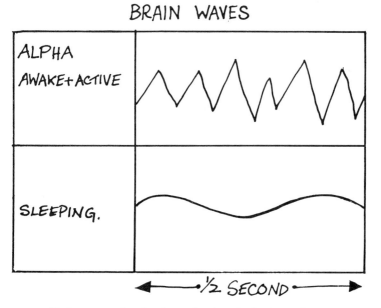

Brain waves plot the electricity that the brain produces
as it works.

skull the brain is protected by a kind of membrane round which laps the cerebrospinal fluid, a clear fluid that flows through the brain.

This book is about how the brain works and affects the way

that we see, hear, feel, talk, touch and behave. One way to imagine this is to picture the brain as a huge board of flashing lights, on which each cell is represented by a light. Every cell has either to be ON – firing and active – or OFF – inactive. The whole display is in a state of constant change.

In the book, we will try and show how curious, complicated, interesting and at times simply *odd* is the way that we – and our senses – are organized.

Vision

We can see amazingly well. When townspeople go into the countryside, they are usually surprised to find how far and how well they can see in the dark. A very dim flash of light that lasts for only one thousandth of a second can easily be seen by moonlight, and a person with normal eyesight can see a candle glowing in the dark well over 100 metres away. In the dark, our eyes become about 10,000 times more sensitive than they are in bright light. But though our eyesight is very good, we are born half blind.

Learning to See

Seeing is second nature to us. Only blind people who have regained their sight remember a time when they could not see. But babies are born no more able to see than they are to speak. The eyes are closed at birth. They open soon afterwards, but only briefly, for most babies spend much of their first week asleep. Only slowly can their eyes get used to the light.

It isn't surprising that this is a slow process, because for nine months, in the womb, the baby has been floating in darkness. When it is born the light must come as something of a shock. In fact, the eyes are better developed at birth than almost any other part of the body, but they have had no practice at seeing. And they need that practice.

You cannot *teach* babies how to see; but they have to *learn* how to do it. This is automatic as long as the baby has plenty to see. At birth, a baby can distinguish light from dark. By the age of four weeks, most babies can focus. By six weeks they can see some patterns, like stripes, very well, and by ten weeks they can usually follow an object as it moves. So babies do learn quickly.

By the age of four months, babies can recognize faces quite well: if they are shown masks like those on the next page, they respond with smiles; if they are shown faces with the features mere blocks of colour, jumbled up, or odd patterns, they don't. They can already distinguish the contours of the human face.

No one, thankfully, has tried to carry out experiments in which children have had their vision interfered with 'in the interests of science'. But work with kittens has shown how important it is for the eyes to get plenty of different things to see.

The Spitz experiment: Dr Spitz showed babies masks of human faces. On some the features were in the correct place, on others they were jumbled up. He also showed them blocks of colour and odd patterns. They responded best to the human face with the features in the right place.

Cat's Eyes

In an experiment kittens were brought up in special boxes or drums. The boxes were painted with nothing but square rectangular lines: the drums with nothing but curves. It was found that kittens reared in the 'square world' could not see round or curved lines and that the kittens reared in a 'curved world' could not see straight lines. It is not just general practice at seeing that the eyes need: they need to see specifically different shapes. If kittens do not see these things in the first months of their life, they cannot learn to see them later on. Kittens that were not allowed to walk did even worse. Normally,

of course, the kitten would be exposed to all these different shapes, but if it misses that 'chance', something in the brain, in the eyes, withers, and that is that.

People are more flexible. People who have been blind since birth and suddenly recover their sight do learn to see. But it is a very hard and, often, emotionally trying process.

The Eyes Need to See

Many experiments have been carried out to discover what happens if people are put into total darkness. In Canada, psychologists once placed a series of twenty-nine subjects in a 'black box' – a soundproofed, lightless room. Each subject went into his box alone, wearing goggles to cut out any stray light. How long could they stand it? To encourage them each person got $20 (then £8 and a lot of money) for each day he, or she, managed to complete 'inside' the box.

Few people lasted thirty-six hours though a few survived for three days. Twenty-five of the twenty-nine said that they had 'seen things' during the time they were in their box. What they had seen varied from dots and flickering lights to quite complex scenes. One man saw a cartoon, over and over again. Not every study of what happens to people in 'black boxes' has come up with the same results, but most of them tend the same way.

The results suggest that when there is nothing real for our eyes to see, they 'invent' things. The eyes need to be active. The longer you wear goggles, the more likely you are to make up for the lack of visual stimuli by having hallucinations.

So, eyes need practice. They need to learn how to put together all the patterns we see and to make sense of them. They then need to keep on seeing. Only the initial learning is automatic – every time a baby sees a toy, and reaches out for it, he is learning something about the relationship between what a thing looks like and how far away it is. But the baby is not conscious of it. When a child can speak, he will have forgotten the fact that there was a time when he could not see as effortlessly as he does now.

What the Eye is Made Of

The eye is part of the brain, and is the only part of it that you can touch. The visible ear is a flap of skin that does nothing; the real ear is the inner ear inside the skull. But the eye is an outpost of the brain. The cells of the retina are directly connected to areas of the brain.

What happens when light falls on to the eye? To try and explain this, the eye is often compared to a camera. Light passes through the lens of a camera and falls on to a sensitive plate at the back. In most modern cameras, the film itself is this plate. Depending on how much light there is, the photographer changes the size of the lens aperture or opening. If too much light is let in, the picture will be too white or over-exposed: if too little light is let in, the picture will be dark. Changing the size of your lens aperture allows you to adjust the amount of light you have.

The eye operates on the same principle. Light passes through the pupil and then through a lens. The curved surface of the lens bends the light to focus it on the retina, which is the sensitive plate of the eye. The muscles of the eye can adjust both the size of the pupil, and the extent to which the lens is curved, to let more or less light in. You don't consciously

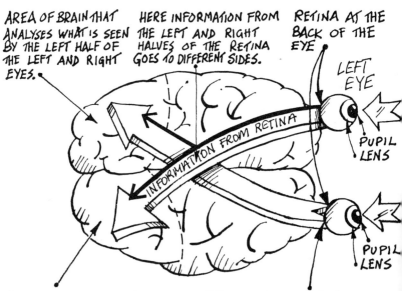

AREA OF BRAIN THAT ANALYSES WHAT IS SEEN BY THE LEFT HALF OF THE LEFT AND RIGHT EYES.

HERE INFORMATION FROM THE LEFT AND RIGHT HALVES OF THE RETINA GOES TO DIFFERENT SIDES.

RETINA AT THE BACK OF THE EYE

LEFT EYE

INFORMATION FROM RETINA

PUPIL
LENS

PUPIL
LENS

AREA OF BRAIN THAT ANALYSES WHAT IS SEEN BY THE RIGHT HALF OF THE LEFT AND RIGHT EYES.

THE IMAGE ON THE RETINA IS BROKEN DOWN INTO ELECTRICAL AND CHEMICAL MESSAGES WHICH GO TO THE BACK OF THE BRAIN.

adjust your eyes as you do a camera; but the principle is the same.

The comparison between the eye and the camera soon breaks down, however. True, you can look into a person's eyes and see a picture there; but this picture is not what he in fact sees.

Double Vision

Each eye has a retina. And on each retina there is an upside-down image.

Two retinas, two images. Each of these images is full of things that we don't actually see – for example, there is a filing cabinet on the image of my right retina but it is only now that I notice it and 'see' it. I was looking at the table. But the filing cabinet has been there all along for me to see.

If you were to take a photo of a person's eyes when he is looking at a table, you would see a table in each eye. If you had a table in two lenses you would expect to end up with a picture of two tables. Two table images (photographically) should produce two tables in the picture. So it is extraordinary, given that we have two eyes and that each sees pretty much the same image, that we only see one table. If someone does see two tables when he is only looking at one, something is wrong; he is suffering from 'double vision'. Two tables aren't a bonus. Only if people are drunk or ill or very, very tired do they see double. (It is actually very hard to see double deliberately. You have to squint for perhaps thirty seconds, and even then you may not succeed.)

Not only do we have the two images, but they are upside down. It is still not known just how the brain turns what the retina sees the right way up. But what is clear is that it takes a great deal of very complicated, high-speed 'computing' to make what we in fact see out of the images that fall on the retina.

If the brain did not do this we would see a topsy-turvy world twice over. And a creature with such bad eyesight wouldn't have survived very long!

How does the light that falls on the eye get changed so that within a few milliseconds of a table coming into our field of vision, we know that we're seeing a table?

Inside the Retina

There are many different kinds of cells in the eye. The two most important are called the rods and cones, which are, as their names suggest, rod- and cone-shaped. Every rod and cone is filled with a small amount of pigment. One can imagine each of them as a tiny jar filled with coloured water.

Both the rods and the cones lie on the outside of the eyeball, facing outwards. When the light hits a rod or a cone, it bleaches out the pigment in it: the light 'makes' the pigment flow out, and within a few milliseconds the rod or cone is bleached dry. It is this process that starts up the biochemical reactions at the back of the retina which, in their turn, pass information up into the brain.

At the back of the eye the images on the retina are broken down into a series of messages in a complicated code and then passed on, in the form of electrical impulses and biochemical reactions. See the diagram on page 18.

Soldiers who had been injured and suffered damage to a certain part of the brain found themselves going blind or seeing very badly. Nothing was wrong with their eyes, but

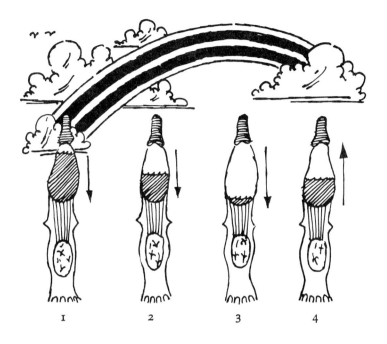

When a cone 'sees' colour, its pigment is bleached away
as in 1, 2 and 3. Then it fills up with pigment again.

the part of the brain that decoded the messages from the eyes
and converted them into the experience of seeing had stopped
working properly. They could not see.

The eye then does not 'do' all our seeing.

No one knows how this or any other part of the brain turns
the electrical and chemical messages it receives into the experience that we are conscious of having. For a long time
scientists thought that if they could describe everything that
happened in the brain when one, for example, saw a red line
moving, they would know what it is to see a red line moving.

But the brain does not see. You see. I see. Knowing precisely what goes on in the brain when we are seeing is not the same thing. It does not explain how it is that I see and *know* that I am seeing. I can't actually see and not know it, but though that is part of my experience of seeing, it is not accounted for in any way by the messages and firings of cells that are happening as I see.

The brain breaks up the image of the car. We know a lot about the way the image is broken up in the brain, but we do not really know how the brain puts it all together again so that we 'see' the car.

It is difficult, and important, to understand this difference. Scientists know enough to draw a map of the brain rather like a map of an underground system. The map is not complete. Some stations are missing. Many but not all trains that are running are marked. It is a good map, better than any previous one but not perfect. From the outside, we partly understand this railway system. A railway, of course, is not at all like a person. A railway system does not know it exists though, of course, the travellers on it know that it exists. What is missing in our map of the brain when it comes to seeing? First, an explanation of how the brain converts all these messages into the obvious but mysterious fact that I am seeing. And, second, how I am aware that I am seeing. The clue to both problems must lie in the way the brain works. But scientists are far from solving these particular questions about the workings of the brain.

Special Cells

Scientists often use animals to find out what is happening inside the brain. In one kind of experiment, a small hole is bored through the skull of an animal, and a small electrode or recording device is lowered through this hole into the visual cortex. Scientists can then pass a tiny current through the device to see what is happening to some cells, or even one cell, when, for example, the animal sees a circle or a straight line. The animal is in no pain during this experiment.

By examining the visual cortex in this way, scientists have found a whole host of very specialized cells which only fire when they see a particular pattern. For example, some cells only fire when they see straight lines; others fire for moving lines; others for corners or squares. A cell that is firing when it sees a line at an angle of 60° may not respond to a line at an angle of 30°. Some cells respond only to lines moving to the left, others to lines moving to the right, others to diagonally moving lines. Anything the eye sees is bound to trigger some – but only some – of the cells.

The pattern formed by the firing cells must then be deciphered by more complex cells before it makes any sense. These more complex cells, in some as yet unknown way, decode exactly what the pattern we are seeing is. But how we know that it is a table we are seeing and how we *know* that we are seeing a table remains a mystery . . .

The brain re-combines what the eyes have told it in such a way that we know we're seeing a table. But the exact way it achieves this is still a mystery.

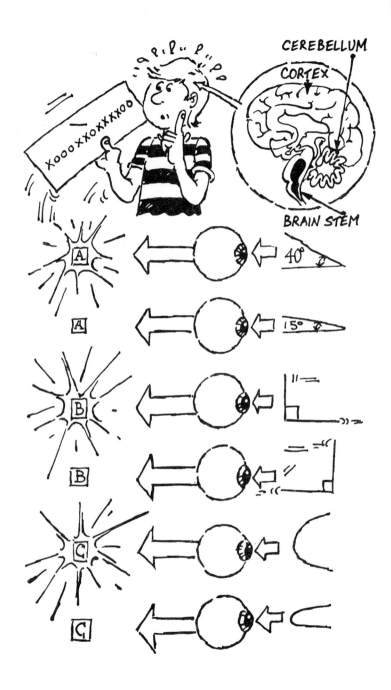

Do It Yourself

Close all the curtains in your room. Turn off the light. Shut the door. Block off any source of stray light. Wait ten minutes.

First, see what you can see. Try to determine how accurately you can see in the dark. Can you see colours at all? What things that you know are there can you not see?

Now turn all the lights in the room on. To get the best effect, you need at least two – and preferably three – lights, each of 100 watts. At first your eyes will feel a little dazzled. Try and tell whether they become drier or more moist. Probably they will feel very dry when you turn the lights on; then you may feel a moistening. If you go into the light, your eyes have to blink and close. This is a defensive reaction: the eyes need to adapt to the light. The pigment in the cones – hardly used when you look in the dark – needs to flood back, and this takes time. Equally, it takes time to get used to the dark. At first, you see very little. Slowly, your eyes adapt and sight improves.

Secondly, look out of your window. Either close one eye or wear a patch over one eye. When you look at things with one eye, they may seem a little blurred in the distance. But if you ask people to judge the distance of things with only one eye, they are still very good at it . . .

Seeing in the Distance,
or Two Eyes are Better than One

One of the reasons we have two eyes is in order to see more and to see more accurately. As the brain evolved, it must have

In A, B and C, one of the things the eye sees fires a cell. 15° is too small an angle to fire cell A. The second right angle is the wrong way round to fire cell B. The curve is too narrow to fire cell C.

seemed worth suffering all the problems that two eyes caused in return for greater accuracy and scope of vision.

To get a really sharp picture of the tree, the eyes have to converge on it. This means that we don't see well out of the 'corners' of our eyes. It is nearly impossible to use one's eyes so that the right looks at one thing and the left at another, which would be a perfectly logical way of using two eyes. What we do is to use both eyes and then *move them* to look at the next thing, performing a quick and intricate sequence of events.

First, an object appears far from the centre of our vision. The outside part of the eye – the periphery – notices something and notices enough about it to tell us that it needs looking at. Next, we move so that both our eyes can see it. We don't consciously decide to move our eyes; it happens automatically. The process takes 100 milliseconds or less, about the time that a world champion sprinter in full stride would take to run a metre. Unless you are actually thinking about it, you will not notice you are doing it.

The process of seeing has to be quick. We have to be able to see cars out of the corner of our eyes, look at them properly, and then move fast enough to avoid them. Early man had the same problem with lions, leopards, tigers and countless other hungry beasts. He had to spot them, see them and spear them, or we would not be here working out how it is that the eye works!

When your eyes converge on an object to see it sharply, they are turned in at an angle. To get an idea of the angle, try the experiment on the next page.

Do It Yourself

Look at something in the far distance. Then, quickly, look at your thumb 8cm in front of you. Do it a number of times. You should be able to feel your eyes, and your eye muscles, moving. They have to move because as your focus shifts from the far distance to your thumb at 8 cm the angle at which your eyes are turned changes – and does so radically.

When you look into the distance, your eyes are hardly turned in at all. But when you look at your thumb, or at anything quite close, the angle at which your eyes are turned in is acute. We 'know' how distant things are because our brain registers the angle at which the eyes are turned to focus on an object. It knows the distance between our right and our left eye, and can work out the distance of the object that is seen – just as you would calculate the angles of a triangle given a base line and a point to work from.

Small babies spend much of their time reaching for objects. Without knowing it they are learning to coordinate sight and touch so that they can judge how far away things are. A nine-month old baby will have an excellent idea of whether he can grasp a ball by reaching out his arm or whether he has to crawl a metre to be able to get at it. Imagine what it would be like if you could not tell how far away the teapot was, for instance, and started to reach for it three metres away! We take our ability to make judgements like this for granted. The rider on a bicycle needs to know how far away other objects on the road are. This can be complicated as he is moving at one speed and the cars at different speeds and in different directions. No one thinks this is very difficult, because it comes naturally, but we forget that it is something we must learn. As we move, we learn. Activity is crucial. No baby is born able to judge distances; but this skill is acquired at such an early age, and becomes so automatic, that it seems it was there from birth.

The angle the eyes make when looking at an object is not the only clue we have. When we look at an object in the distance with just one eye, the eye has to turn itself to focus on the

object. But as well as the angle that the one eye makes, we use our own experience. We know how far away most objects in a particular scene are *likely* to be. Our eyes know something about perspective – for example, things slope away in the distance because of the curvature of the earth. But because we rely on the way we normally see things, we can be fooled.

Tricks ...

Psychologists enjoy playing tricks on people. In studying vision, tricks can be useful since they can show how we normally use our eyes. Both these straight lines are the same length. But the arrows fool you into thinking the top one is longer.

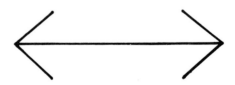

Colour Vision

Most people can see a full range of colours, light greens, dark reds, deep purple, light blues and all other hues. We also see black and white. About 4 per cent of the population is colour-blind to some extent. Most colour-blind people confuse, or fail to see, red and green as two separate colours. To them they appear either as shades of red or shades of green.

Not only can we *see* colours, we can make very fine distinctions between them. Psychologists have found that most subjects can see some thirty-five different hues between purple and light blue, and nearly 100 different hues of such basic colours as red and yellow.

Before trying to understand how the eye can see such detail of colour, we have to understand how colours are made up. Sir Isaac Newton (1642–1727), one of the most renowned scientists of all time, discovered that if you mix all the lights from all the colours in the spectrum – red, green, yellow, blue, purple – you get white light. Indeed, if you pass white light through a prism, it breaks up into all these different coloured lights. White light is very different from white paint, which can't break up into all, or any, of the colours of the rainbow.

Long after Newton, it was discovered that by mixing the lights of only three colours – red, green and blue – it was possible to get most of the hues that people could see. This suggests that the eye needs only three specialized cones – each of which is sensitive to one of these colours – for us to see in colour the way we do. If a person is colour-blind, it is because one set of these receptors is not working properly.

This kind of theory was first suggested in 1801 by Thomas Young, a child prodigy who had taught himself to read English, French and Greek by the time he was five, and had become

Professor at the Royal Institution – then the most prestigious scientific research institute in Britain – by the age of twenty. Young proposed that there were three separate kinds of cone: one for red, one for green, one for blue. It was not then clear that each of these receptors is only *more sensitive* to its own colour and not totally blind to the other colours. By and large, Young's basic idea holds true.

If you test which parts of the eye can see in colour, it soon becomes clear that the periphery of the eye sees only in black, white and shades of grey. Colour vision depends on seeing out of the *centre* of the eye where the cones are concentrated. It is the cones that see colour. When we see in the dark, we use the rods whose pigment is purple. In the dark we don't see in colour.

Light travels in waves, rather like the waves of the ocean, and the colour of the light depends on the size of the wave. There seem to be three different kinds of cone, each most sensitive to a particular wave-length of light: one for blue (short waves), one for green (longer) and one for near-red (longer still). By mixing light of these three wave-lengths it seems to be possible to make up every visible hue. Of course, the fact that the cones are *most* sensitive to light of a particular wave-length means that they are also *fairly* sensitive to colours whose wave-lengths are in the same range. No separate cone has been found which is most sensitive to yellow.

What happens when a ray of coloured light hits the eye? If you look at a green object, part of the green light that comes from the object will land on a green cone, where its arrival will start a process of bleaching. The green light bleaches out the green-sensitive pigment in the cone, usually in a few milli-seconds. The biochemical signals set up by this process of bleaching indicate to the brain what colour is being seen. When you are looking at an array of coloured objects, you have to

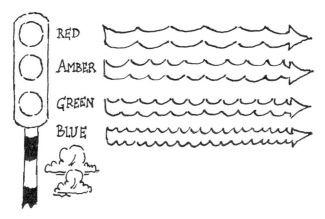

Each colour is made of light waves of a different length. The longer the wave-length the redder the light.

imagine a most spectacular and rapid series of messages, stemming from the biochemical breakdown of pigments in cones all over the front part of the retina, which are passed into the brain for decoding.

After the pigment has been bleached out of the cone, it regenerates within a few milliseconds. At any one time, there have to be cones that are able to see the colour they are most sensitive to, or the colour of the world around us would keep changing. If all the green-sensitive cones were drained of pigment (even for one second) after seeing green grass, the grass would then turn grey; as the pigment regenerated, the grass would turn green again. Nice at a fun-fair – but most inconvenient if you had to live like that permanently. It seems that the cones lose their pigments and regenerate them in different time sequences so that the stock of 'green paint' is never fully used up. The same goes for the red- and the blue-sensitive pigment. Among the 120 million cones in each eye, there are always some which are, as it were, ready to see.

33

Most of the research on colour vision is based on studies of animals and their eyes. Cruel as it may sound, you can dissect the living eye of a frog. You cannot study the human eye in the same way.

To See is to Notice

So we learn to see. The human infant spends most of his first four months learning to focus on objects, learning to follow them and learning to put together what he sees with what he touches so that he builds up a picture of the world. But it is not just a matter of all the connections being made in his brain: it is also a question of what he notices.

As I write, I am looking at the table in front of me. On it, there is a record player, a typewriter, a tape-recorder and its microphone. There is a heap of papers. I have been working here for two hours. But it is only now, as I am looking for examples to illustrate this point, that I 'see' that there is also a candlestick, a pair of sunglasses and a copy of a book called *The Haunted House*. It isn't that these objects have not before 'hit' my retina. Light from them has gone through my eyes. In the last two hours, I must have scanned back and forth past them countless times. But I have not *noticed* them. There has been no reason for me to notice them. They become obvious now because I am trying to illustrate the point that we see only what we choose and need to see.

The eye is not itself selective but the brain has to be. It could not cope with decoding every message about every thing, scene or relation that the eyes see. The brain filters out visual information which is not important and can afford not to be seen. What is filtered out depends on the circumstances.

34

If you are in danger of being run down, you are likely to 'see' only the car coming towards you.

If you are trying to follow a game of football on the television, you are not likely to 'see' the cat curled up in a corner of the room.

We see what we want and expect to see. Imagine that you are waiting for a friend in a crowded place. You think your friend will be wearing a red shirt, so every time you see someone vaguely his shape and size who is wearing red, you expect it to be your friend. You may even think it *is* your friend until he gets close. Then you realize it is not. We say 'your eyes deceived you'. But it isn't the eyes who are guilty at all, it is the brain.

Many newspapers carry quizzes in which people are asked to spot ten mistakes in the second picture, and it is often quite hard to do. Normally, we look and decide very quickly that a car is a car. Then, we assume it has four round wheels, a steering wheel, windows and so on. If it has three round wheels and a square one, you may easily fail to 'see' the square wheel. It isn't that the image of the square wheel has somehow failed to get on to the retina. It is just that everything else looks so much like a car that you expect it to be a car, and don't notice the flaws.

Do It Yourself

A good way to test this is to write a number of cards out with 'almost-words' on them. An almost-word would be something like SONE – which might be *some* – or WORL – which might be *word* or *work* – or PANF – which might be *pant* or *pans*. Once you have the idea of almost-words, you can make them up very quickly. Write one almost-word on a card. Make up ten cards. Then show them very quickly to people and ask them to tell you what it says on the card. In a psychology experiment, the cards would be shown quickly by a machine called a tachisto-scope, which can expose them for as little as five milliseconds.

You will find that people tend to see real words provided you can flash them by hand for a short enough time.

Smell and Taste

How Do We Smell?

Not as well as many animals.

If you go into a room that is 10m by 7m by 3m high into which 1/25,000,000,000 milligram of a chemical called mercaptan has been released, you will be able to smell this tiny, tiny amount. The smell will be nasty and rather like gas. Because the human nose can smell out such minute quantities of mercaptan, it is mixed in with gas in order to make gas leaks easier to detect.

But, despite this feat, we smell very badly compared to many animals. For a dog, the world is a world of smells. Dr Doolittle fans may remember the prodigious smelling feats of Jip, the dog who once managed to sniff out a man across hundreds of miles of open sea by smelling the tobacco he used. That was perhaps stretching the dog's nose a bit far. But it shows well enough how some animals can out-smell us.

Some animals, cats for example, 'see' with their noses. If you watch a cat in a room with a piece of meat, you will notice that it hardly uses its eyes to 'see' where the piece of meat is – even though cats have sharp eyes. If you blindfolded a person and told him to make for the pot of stew which was somewhere in the room, he would probably hesitate and have to make a considerable effort to reach it. He could not place it easily by smell. Unlike dogs and cats, man has never used his nose all that much for hunting. Long ago, when our ancestors roamed the great plains hunting for prey, they relied on their ears and, especially, their eyes, because the human eye is extremely good at spotting moving things. And the more civilized we have become, the less we have come to rely on our sense of smell.

If you would like to test this, jot down one day how often you are conscious of actually smelling something. We can, of course, smell many things – some smells are delicious and others very nasty. But there are very few times when it is important to us to smell something. All that would happen to someone who lost his sense of smell is that his food would taste a little blander and that he could not enjoy perfumes. He would have a much less serious disadvantage in life than someone who went blind, deaf, or lost his sense of touch.

For an organ that has lost most of its usefulness, the nose is a rather wonderful and complicated thing.

The nose consists of two nostrils, each of which is a tunnel; scientists usually speak not of the nose but of the *nasal cavity*.

We use the nostrils day in, day out, for breathing. The two tunnels join at the back of the nose and feed into the top of the mouth. Because of this, you can feel the liquid trickle down the back of your throat when you have nosedrops.

Each of our nostrils is lined with a slimy sort of mucus, which is in almost perpetual slow motion. 'It opens and closes rather like the petals of a flower,' as one writer put it romantically. At the top of the nostrils are what are called the 'olfactory' cells – the 'smelling' cells. They are part of the brain and they take up quite a large area for cells – about 2·5 square centimetres. One hundred million cells are packed into this area, the shape of which resembles a bulb of garlic.

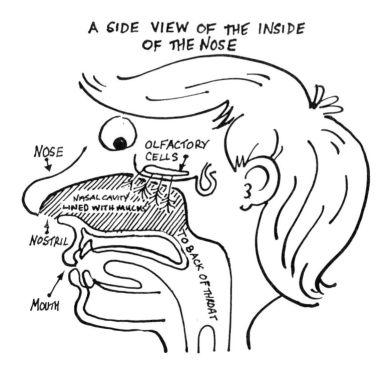

A SIDE VIEW OF THE INSIDE OF THE NOSE

NOSE

OLFACTORY CELLS

NASAL CAVITY LINED WITH MUCUS

TO BACK OF THROAT

NOSTRIL

MOUTH

These cells project tiny hairs into the mucus – each hair is something like 1/100th the size of one of the hairs on your head. Specific chemicals on these hairs react to the smells in the air to make you smell a particular smell.

The latest theory of smell argues that three things have to happen for us to become aware of a smell. First, what is to be smelled has to be volatile, or changeable; it has to be a substance which can release molecules into the atmosphere, because it is the molecules which have left the original substances that find their way into the nose. (Lead and glass don't usually smell because their structure is firm; their molecules stay locked inside the material.) Secondly, the molecules have to be absorbed by the cells in the nose, which means they can be mixed with water. Thirdly, they must be noticed by the olfactory cells because the scent they carry marks a change from the scents which are already around. The nose is full of water, for example, so if you try to smell water you will not have any sensation of smell. Water makes no impact because it registers no change. Also our nose gets used to the most horrid smells. After five minutes the most putrid smell smells not quite so bad.

The picture on the opposite page shows how we experience smells.

No one has mapped all the smells that we can smell. The nose can smell quite new substances. Eighteenth-century man, for example, never had the pleasure of smelling the exhaust fumes of a car! Nevertheless, some scientists have tried to work out the basic smells that we can smell. There seem to be seven: camphoraceous (like moth-balls); musky; floral; pepperminty; ethereal-like; pungent; putrid.

The scientists who devised this list believe that all possible smells can be created by mixing these basic scents. No one is really sure that it is true, but it is an interesting idea. We seem

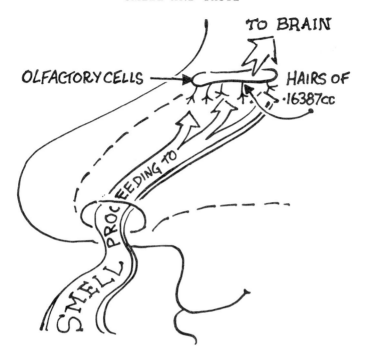

TO BRAIN

OLFACTORY CELLS

HAIRS OF
.16387cc

FEEDING TO

SMELL PROC...

to see three basic colours as well as black and white and to taste four basic tastes – everything else that we see and taste can be produced by mixing these elements. Perhaps our smell follows a similar pattern.

Do It Yourself

Get hold of some of the following: garlic; mint; moth-balls; chocolate. Put each substance in a small glass container without any label. When your friends next come and see you ask them to tell you what they are smelling. That will show you how well we can recognize smells in isolation.

Why We Smell

Although the nose has become more and more useless in one sense, throughout history people have tried to make themselves smell more attractive.

The modern perfume industry has a long history. Making perfume is one of the oldest businesses we know about. Round about 3000 BC the ancient Egyptians were already masters of the art. They spent much time and money creating sweet-smelling skin creams called unguents. Their purpose was not much different from that of the hundreds of perfumes, eau-de-Colognes and after-shave lotions that are sold today. They were used to mask the normal smells of the body, even if some of them, like sweat, can actually be quite pleasant.

This passion for smelling nice has often been carried to excess. The Roman emperor Nero drenched himself in so much

incense at the funeral of his mistress, Poppea, that he was said to have used as much incense as Arabia could produce in ten years. At banquets, Nero would have his slaves shower guests with the petals of sweet-smelling flowers. In olden days, the confetti thrown at a married couple were flowers, which were supposed to make them smell sweet for each other.

The reason for this accent on perfume seems to be that there is a connection between some smells and sexual attractiveness. Monkeys use scent as a way of telling other monkeys that they are ready and willing to have sex. Animals seem to secrete various kinds of sweat and other substances specifically for this purpose. We have learned – or the cosmetic industry has tried to teach us – to think of these natural odours as repulsive. If you smell of yourself, no one will love you, and since we all feel very insecure about being loved, we cover ourselves with all kinds of unnatural scents.

In nature, however, the things that smell bad and, often, taste bitter do so because they are dangerous. Arsenic, for instance, is about the only poison that does not taste so horrible that it will normally be spat out. Dead bodies smell extremely unpleasant, and this puts off most animals and men from eating them – which is just as well, as the decaying meat would probably be highly poisonous. The smells that our bodies give off, however, are not naturally unpleasant (unless you never wash). But we are beginning to think of them as unpleasant, so that in order to be attractive to other people, we think we have to mask many of the smells which nature has 'given' us precisely so that we can attract others sexually.

Taste

Our tongues have not become as redundant as our noses. We use our tongues for two main purposes – to eat and to speak. Since our ancestors must have learned to eat long before they could speak, we may safely assume that the tongue is, first and foremost, an organ to taste with.

The tongue is a rough patch of muscle, membrane and fat that is full of pits and grooves. Within these pits and grooves lie the taste buds, which project tiny hairs on to the surface of the tongue. These hairs are about the same size as the hairs the olfactory cells project. Each taste bud contains about twenty taste cells. These cells seem to be in a constant state of decay and birth. At one time, some of the taste cells will be immature, some will be mature and some will be decaying. The cells near the centre of the taste bud are usually the ones that have grown to maturity but have not yet started to decay.

There are many millions of taste buds on each human tongue.

The tip of the tongue

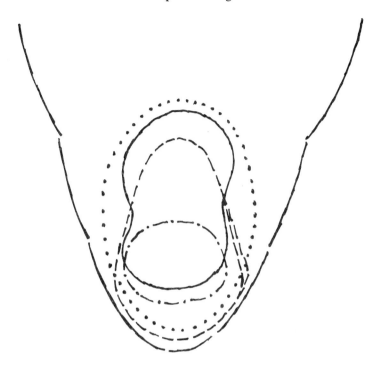

————————	INSIDE THIS AREA THE TASTE BUDS DO NOT REACT TO SWEET FLAVOURS
• • • • • • • • • •	INSIDE THIS AREA THE TASTE BUDS DO NOT REACT TO BITTER FLAVOURS
— — — — — —	INSIDE THIS AREA THE TASTE BUDS DO NOT REACT TO SALTY FLAVOURS
• — • — • — • —	INSIDE THIS AREA THE TASTE BUDS DO NOT REACT TO SOUR FLAVOURS

We seem to be aware of four basic tastes: sour, salty, sweet and bitter. Each area of the tongue – and some of the buds – appears to respond best to a certain sort of taste. The tip of the tongue seems to be particularly good at tasting sweet things and rejecting bitter things. There are good reasons for this. Before sweets became the plague of our teeth, sugar was an important source of food energy. Animals like the taste so that they are motivated to seek it out. And it is important to taste bitterness fast because many bitter things are poisonous. For our own protection we can detect bitterness far more easily than salty, sweet or sour tastes. Normally, an animal that is given a bitter-tasting substance as food will reject it.

Do It Yourself

Put four glasses of water in front of you. In glass 1, place 5g of ordinary white sugar. In glass 2, place 5g of salt. In glass 3, place 5g of lemon juice. In glass 4, place 2g of something bitter like angostura bitters.

Ask your friends to tell you what each solution tastes of. They will probably not be able to taste anything in glasses 1 to 3. See how much more sugar, salt and lemon juice you have to place in each glass until they can detect it. They will easily taste the angostura bitters.

Although the tongue has areas which are much better at tasting one of these basic sensations than the others, it is not simply that we have one set of buds for sweet, one for sour, one for bitter and one for salt.

These graphs show the way two different buds react to each of the four basic tastes. A is not just a 'salty' bud; it also has

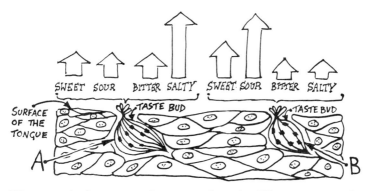

These two buds react, as the arrows show, in different ways to the different tastes. A *salty* taste makes A jump high but the other tastes do not affect it very much. B is stimulated by *sour*, gets quite a lot out of *sweet*, but hardly notices *bitter* or *salty*. Different buds, different tastes!

some reaction to sweet, sour and bitter. B is not just a 'sour' bud: it reacts quite well to sugar, though hardly at all to bitter and salty. The taste we experience depends on the intensity of response of taste buds to the different substances. For instance, a taste system made up of bud A and bud B could taste something sweet provided that when taste B 'tasted' sugar it did not also have to taste something sour that would overwhelm the sweet taste.

The fact that the taste system seems to be so organized explains why we can actually experience different tastes at the same time. To test this chew an olive at the same time as you are eating a grape. Our appetite appears to be stimulated by having different kinds of things to eat one after the other. The reason is simple. Just as we get used to smells very quickly, so we get used to tastes very quickly. Half a minute after you have drunk a solution with 10g of sugar dissolved in it, you need

47

to drink something with 13g of sugar dissolved to get the feeling that it is just as sweet. Contrasting tastes set one another off very successfully.

Gourmets who like to plan their food as a sensual experience make sure that every course has a different kind of taste. A big meal might well go something like this:

Hors d'œuvre – cold and rather sharp
Soup – warm and mellow
Meat – warm and often spicy
Salad – usually with a sharp vinegary dressing
Cheese – which can be smooth and bland, or quite sharp and salty, but always has a distinctive taste
Sweet – sweet
A savoury – often salty to balance the sweetness of the sweet

Good cooks have an accurate sense of what tastes particularly good from one course to the next. In the past, great cooks knew how to orchestrate the taste buds of their customers.

The Right Amount of the Right Food

Man seems to be one of the few species that has to teach its young to eat properly. Most animals know instinctively what and how much they should eat. In 1944, a scientist kept rats in cages. The food cups in the cages contained purified, and tasteless, 'foods' that could make up an adequate diet: protein, fat, dried yeast, carbohydrates and ten other substances. The rats were left free to eat whatever they liked. They all chose a perfect, nutritionally balanced diet.

There are similar stories about human children. One tragic

one was about a baby who kept grabbing salty food and whose first spoken word was *salt*. He was taken to hospital to stay and, there, on the hospital diet, he received far less salt than usual. He died very quickly. It was discovered then that he suffered from a rare disease that caused a salt deficiency. He knew what he needed to live much better than the doctors.

In the wild, salt is a rare and essential food. Large herds of animals have been known to undertake dramatic migrations in search of it.

We have forgotten the art of eating properly. It must be ironic for an Asian peasant to learn that, while he is in danger of starvation, the 'slimming' business is worth millions of dollars in the U S A and millions of pounds in Britain every year. One half of the world starves; the other half overeats.

It is certainly true that we have lost the art of instinctive feeding. In an experiment with young children, it was found

that once they reached the age of fifteen months, they were very bad at feeding themselves. They concentrated on sweet food which often had very little food value, and tended to be put off by a number of foods which were good for them, like carrots, meat and cheese.

As children, we have to be taught which berries it is dangerous to eat. We have no instinct for it – again, unlike animals. People seem to have forgotten – perhaps we have learned to forget – what we once knew naturally about feeding ourselves.

It isn't that animals have no food preferences. Even the lowly earthworm prefers carrot leaves to celery leaves and celery leaves to cabbage. As for fish, most of the scales of their body have taste buds on them so that they are able to 'taste' the sea they are swimming in.

Why We Overeat

There are many theories about why people eat too much. People may overeat because they are too anxious, because they are bored or even because they want to impress. In our society, the jolly fat man is supposed to be not perhaps a picture of health but at least contented and prosperous. He has to be able to afford to eat too much. In poor countries, fat is beautiful partly because to be fat is a sign of wealth. No one has really proved why we overeat though one of the more cruel theories is that people overeat to console themselves for the fact that they are unloved. Because they eat too much, they get more unlovely and, probably, less lovable. To console themselves, they eat yet more . . . No one can say which of these very briefly outlined theories is true. What is true is that we have lost the proper use of our sense of taste.

Communication

In the eighteenth century, in the south of France, a doctor in the small town of Averyon found a 'wild' boy who was about eight years old. It was hard to be sure of his age because when the boy was found, he was crawling on all fours and making noises like a wolf. He seemed to have been a member of a wolf pack. Locals remembered stories about a 'lost' child, and this seemed to be the child. The doctor decided he would make the wolf-boy human.

He devoted himself to this task, and he had a lot of success. The boy learned to walk on two legs, to wash and dress himself and to respond to discipline. The doctor even taught him to use a knife and fork at table. But the one thing which the doctor failed to do was to teach him to speak. In a number of other cases in which children, probably between the ages of eight and ten, have been found wild, doctors have been unable to teach them how to speak. By eight, it's too late, it seems. The wolf-boy could never really become quite human, for to speak is one of the characteristics of a human being. Most of those who are unfortunate enough to be born mute or dumb still manage to speak in their own language – sign language.

In his famous book *The Naked Ape*, Desmond Morris argues that man is really a naked ape; but what sets us apart from the apes isn't just that we've lost most of the hair and fur which once covered us, it's also that we can speak. Apes we may be, but at least we're talking apes.

The Talk of Bees and Apes

Humans are the only species that can talk. Animals can communicate but the 'language' they can use is very limited. Consider, for example, the bee.

In the 1950s, there was great excitement when scientists discovered that the dance of the bee had some meaning. It wasn't just pointless exercise but the way in which one bee got a message over to the rest of its hive. A bee who had found flowers could tell its fellow bees the direction in which the flowers were and how far away they were. The direction in which the bee's tail pointed indicated the direction they had to fly: the number of wiggles of the bee's tail indicated how far away the flowers were.

So bees can communicate. Their dance is a 'language'. But it's a language in which you can only say three basic things: one, there are flowers; two, the flowers are that way; three, the

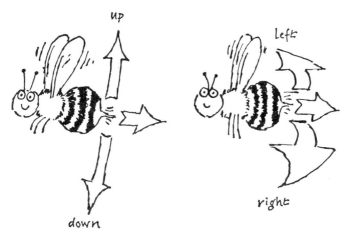

up

down

left

right

The number of wiggles indicates the distance of the flowers.

The direction of the tail indicates the direction of the flowers.

Lots of flowers
200 metres over
there

flowers are that far away. It's not much of a language if that's all you can say in it. It is so inflexible it is really stretching words to call it a language at all.

The bee is not the only non-human creature to be able to use such simple communication. Birds can use their songs to say something. The warbling of many birds serves to tell others something like: 'This branch is mine.' Birds also sing to attract mates; different notes convey the message: 'I'm available.' But, again, this is hardly a language.

Traffic lights, after all, can say something. Depending on how they are lit up, they can declare STOP, WAIT or GO. But we don't think traffic lights have a language. They are merely a set of signals, and cannot be combined to make any different message. For example, if you had all three lights on, it wouldn't mean anything new. Animal 'languages' are the same. They have one specific sound for one fairly specific thing. They are largely inflexible.

Scientists have found that chimpanzees and other ape species can make anything up to thirty-two different sounds. Apes certainly do have a signal to tell each other that a dangerous animal is near and that they ought to flee. Baboons do this by flapping their arms and squeaking or screeching. But no species of ape combines its sounds and grunts to make more complicated signals in the way that a small child will learn to put together words like *want* and *chocolate* to demand: 'Want chocolate.'

In the wild, monkeys and apes (who are, after all, our closest kin in the animal world) get along quite well without any language. If two chimps see a source of food, one may point out its direction. But that is not quite conversation.

In some ways, chimpanzees resemble humans. Baby chimps play as much as human babies do. When a chimp is born, it is more advanced than a human child and it stays ahead until the time that a baby usually starts to speak. But though chimps do enjoy playing, they seem to have no instinct to babble. Babies usually start to babble when they are four or five months old. Some psychologists believe that even before this they are trying to speak. Chimps seem to have no such need.

As chimps have exactly the same brain as us, psychologists have quite often tried to bring up a chimp as a baby. One family of psychologists, the Kelloggs, talked to their baby chimp as they did to their own baby. The chimp fitted in quite well with the family. She was toilet trained, she played, and she became fond of her human mum and dad. But all the chimp managed to learn was to associate a few grunts with very simple words. The chimp managed to master words something like *cup* or *bed* or *food*. But she did not begin to talk in sentences. For all the drilling the psychologists did they could not teach the chimp to speak.

Recently there have been a number of attempts to teach chimps sign languages, especially American deaf and dumb languages. These have been more successful. Two chimps have

even conversed in deaf and dumb talk. But this seems to be a very unnatural activity for the chimps, and the kind of talk the brightest chimp has mastered by the age of six or seven is only a shadow of the kind of speech a two-year-old child can produce.

But though we now have two chimps engaging in something like conversation, the whole exercise is rather like teaching a pigeon to play the scales on a piano. It can be done. Doing it gives us an insight into what animals can be trained to do. But, in the wild, animals don't do it. It is not natural to them.

But language comes very naturally to man. Scientists have yet to come across a tribe so backward that it has no language. There are still tribes living in what we arrogantly call 'Stone-Age conditions', but not one of them has been unable to speak. Their languages may even turn out to be rather beautiful and poetic. Nor are they simple languages. Many American Indian languages, for example, are very rich and can express the moods of nature well. They may not have a word for *computer* or *retro-rocket* but they have to cater for a very different environment.

The Origins of Language

Given that to talk seems a condition of being human, it is not surprising that we are curious about why, how and when our ancestors started to speak. Because the signals and 'languages' animals use are so unlike human language, they offer little clue as to its origins.

No one knows, of course, who the first man or woman to speak was. There is no way of finding out which tribe was the first to develop a language. Archaeologists have dated the first bits of writing which have been dug up – on gravestones and clay tablets. But we learned to write long after we learned to speak; many primitive tribes have a spoken but not a written language. Of course, one person can't have invented language: it must have been a very slow process involving thousands of people over thousands of years.

There are a number of possible theories that seek to explain how we started to speak. But none of these theories can be proved; they have to remain inspired guesses.

Early man may have started to imitate sounds he heard around him. The crash of thunder may have been used to say that it looked as though thunder was coming and wasn't it frightening? The sound of a roar of a lion may have been used to say there was a lion near by. And so beware! Perhaps these sounds slowly became our first words.

It has also been suggested that we first used sounds to express our feelings. Coming across a bad smell, our ancestor exclaimed: 'Ugh . . .' Coming across a delicious roast, he smiled: 'Yu – um.' That may have been the beginning of language.

It looks as if it took a very long time to develop the capacity to speak. None of the organs that we use to speak were designed for speaking; speech is a by-product of the organs we use to eat and breathe with.

Some skulls which have recently been dug up in East Africa suggest that as much as two million years ago there were creatures with skulls shaped much like ours, which seem to have housed brains rather like ours. Could they speak? No one knows. It may be that these creatures learned to speak when they began to make and use tools. The best scientists can do is to imagine what kinds of need being able to talk fulfilled for these near-humans.

While we may not know or be able to guess why our ancestors started to speak, it is clear that talking gave them many advantages. They could make plans about hunting. They could make plans about building shelter. They could exchange tips about tools. Males and females could understand the feelings they had for one another, which might be important as they could be separated for longish periods. By the time men and women first started to live in villages, they must have had complicated languages not very different from our own.

Human beings made very complex use of speech long before they could write. Stonehenge was begun, at least, by people who did not even have an alphabet. Many scientists now think that the stones have been laid out in such a way that they form an observatory. By recording when the sun and the moon rose over particular stones, these 'primitive' men, just out of the Stone Age, seem to have been able to predict eclipses of the sun and moon – which must have been terrifying events for people round 3000 BC. The tradition was passed down from one generation to the next by word of mouth. It might not be as good as having books to consult about astronomy but it was a lot better than having no means of communication at all.

Animals have no such skills. An animal who learns some new and spectacular trick can't pass it on – the knowledge must die with him. Language makes it possible for man to convey complicated messages which the signals of animal communication cannot begin to cope with. Without language, one could not have built villages, let alone irrigated the desert or built the Pyramids. The story of the Tower of Babel shows how important language was seen to be at the time the Old Testament was written. The first great poets, like Homer, did not have to write down their verse; it was committed to memory and passed on verbally from one generation to the next.

How the voice is produced.

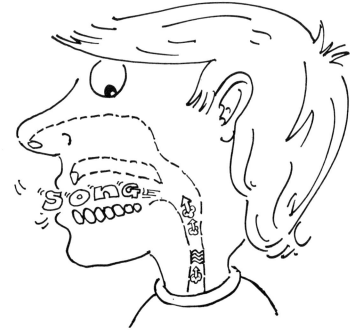

No one, I think, will ever be able to prove that they have solved the mystery of how we started to speak. But that will not stop scientists and others from continuing to guess about it.

Do It Yourself

Stand in front of a mirror.

Watch your face as you go through the vowels – *a, e, i, o, u.*

Note how the shape of your mouth alters.

Say the following consonants very slowly: *p**, then *t* and then the hard *c* or *g* sound, as in *gutter*. Feel what kinds of movements your tongue, lips and teeth are making for each of the consonants.

* To make this sound, start to pronounce the word *pot,* and then break off abruptly.

You will find that *p* is made essentially on the lips and *t* by placing the tongue against the teeth, while hard *c* or *g* is a *guttural* sound made further back in the mouth.

When you say *bug* with its sharp *b* sound, the two lips come close together and then release air. Like *p*, the *b* sound is one that is made on the lips. The *g* sound, on the other hand, is made by bringing up the back of the tongue to the top of the mouth. We make consonants at various points in the mouth or nose cavity; we make vowels by letting air flow freely out of the mouth and changing the shape of the various openings through which the air passes. That is why, when you are standing at the mirror, you will find your mouth forming different shapes.

We use our mouths, and all that is in them, to utter words. But it is our brain that controls how and when we speak. How does it do that?

Speaking Stream

When we speak, we are changing the way the air flows through our mouth and nose cavities. As we breathe in and out, we put obstacles in the way of the air. Most English sounds are made with exhaled air.

At the top of the windpipe in a heavy sheath known as the Adam's Apple is the larynx, or the voice box, which contains the vocal chords. These are bundles of muscle and cartilage, and they can be opened and closed. When the chords are so set that air from the lungs makes them vibrate, you get vocal tone. When we speak, the vocal chords vibrate. The way a person's voice sounds depends a great deal on his vocal chords, for they determine the pitch of his speech.

Some scientists in the nineteenth century thought you could

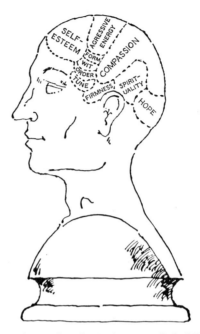

In olden days men knew that the brain controlled different functions. This picture of a phrenologist's head shows the brain divided into what were then thought to be its control centres.

tell a person's character from the bumps on their skull. Each of these bumps was a clue to whether the brain was well developed at a particular point. As the phrenologists believed that each part of the brain controlled one, and only one, aspect of our behaviour, they would find it easy to say that a person with a big bump on the top of his head was very emotional or that someone with a small bump here on one side was low in intelligence. We know now that the brain is not like a department store where there is one counter for Emotions and one for Language and one, say, for Humour. One cannot isolate one kind of activity at one spot inside the skull.

But when scientists first began to look at how language is organized in the brain, they thought they would find one area that contained everything that we needed to speak and to understand language.

In 1861, a French doctor, Paul Broca, was treating a patient who could no longer speak, but only gasp out a few words. Some of his other patients could only talk a long stream of gibberish. Broca examined the brains of a number of these patients after they had died, and found that large areas had become rotten and diseased. Broca thought, therefore, that it was this part of the brain – known as the third frontal convolution – which was responsible for language.

After Broca made this discovery, other surgeons examined after death the brains of patients who had lost their power of speech. It became clear that this part (now known as Broca's area, see below) was mainly responsible for producing speech. Another area was responsible for understanding speech. Other

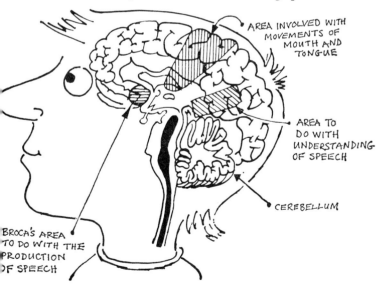

AREA INVOLVED WITH MOVEMENTS OF MOUTH AND TONGUE

AREA TO DO WITH UNDERSTANDING OF SPEECH

CEREBELLUM

BROCA'S AREA TO DO WITH THE PRODUCTION OF SPEECH

areas were responsible for movements of the tongue and vocal chords. Now, it seems clear that all these areas have something to do with how we speak.

Think how many things you do when you talk. You make sounds. You find words to say what you're thinking. You make these words into sentences. You decide just how much you can say in certain situations. You utter the sentences. You watch to see how they affect the people you're speaking to. This list of

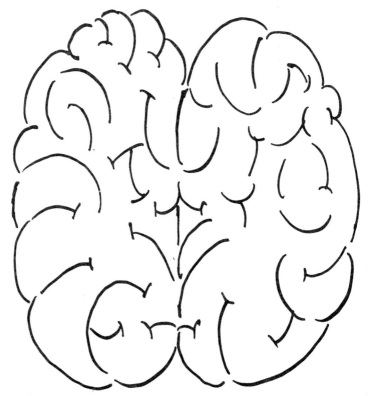

The two cerebral hemispheres. The left hemisphere contains the language area for most right-handed people.

activities involved in talking is far from complete. To have any conversation, you also have to understand what is being said to you.

So it is not surprising that so many parts of the brain should be involved with language. What is more surprising, perhaps, is that for most of us one side of the brain controls language.

The brain has two hemispheres. The left one controls language for all right-handers. If it is damaged in certain areas then language difficulties usually follow. The left hemisphere also controls the right arm. No one knows how it came to control language. Some psychologists think that when men started to talk they also used gestures very expressively. Right-handers would tend to use the right arm for gestures. As primitive language developed side by side with gestures, it was 'taken over' by the left half of the brain, which had controlled the gestures. Interesting guesswork.

To speak and to understand, mouth and mind have to work together. This is not always easy. You may find you've said something you rather wish you hadn't said. You spoke before you thought. Usually, in fact, this is exactly what we do. No one thinks, 'Now I am going to say it's a lovely day' before saying, 'It's a lovely day'. If you do that, it is perhaps a sign that you are nervous or under strain. How do we get to the point where we can speak without thinking?

How We Learn to Talk

A child who never heard people speaking would not learn how to speak. The history books record cases of children who were found wild – often reared by wolves according to legend – and these children could not speak. But what is perhaps more interesting is that a child does not have to be spoken to to learn to speak. Two dedicated psychologists decided to bring up a child without ever speaking to him. The child began to speak quite normally. He had listened to conversations in the house, but neither parent had made an effort – as mothers usually do without being aware of it – to speak to him. It made no difference – the child learned.

When a baby is born, obviously, it does not understand or speak a word. By the age of five, most children can speak their language much like adults do. They may not have as large a vocabulary but they will have mastered the basic sentence forms of the language. This is a remarkable piece of learning by all children, well before they get to school. How does it happen?

Most babies begin to babble a good deal when they are six months old. They enjoy babbling, and often they are fond of one specific sound; my second son adored babbling 'Golly-golly-golly-golly' for minutes on end. Books on how to bring up babies used to frighten parents by telling them at what age

the average baby (whatever that is) started to (i) use one word with meaning (ii) use two-word sentences and (iii) make his first long sentence.

But research has shown that there is a very wide age range within which 'normal' children master various bits of language. In a study of children in Newcastle, these were the ages at which 114 children reached certain talking landmarks.

Thirty-three spoke single words before ten months; forty-two others before twelve months; another twenty-two by eighteen months; but six perfectly normal children had not uttered a word till they were two years old.

Twenty-five children spoke two/three word phrases before sixteen months; another forty-five children before eighteen months; another thirty by two years; but eleven of the children only spoke a two/three word phrase when they were three years old.

A small number of children (10 per cent of the sample) had not developed speech in a fluent way by $4\frac{1}{2}$ years. They went on to develop into perfectly normal children.

The language that children use is interesting in itself. It is a kind of shorthand of normal adult speech. Here is an extract from a tape of a mother and her son, Adam, aged twenty-seven months.

Adam	*Mother*
See truck, Mommy	
See truck	
	Did you see the truck?
No, I see truck	
	No, you didn't see it?
	There goes one
There go one	
	Yes, there goes one

Adam	*Mother*
See a truck	
See truck, Mommy	
See truck	
Truck	
Put truck, Mommy	
	Put the truck where?
Put truck window	
	I think that one's too large to go in the window.

What do we notice about this dialogue?

The way the child speaks is rather like a telegram. If you ran out of money on holiday you wouldn't send a cable that read: I HAVE RUN OUT OF MONEY SO COULD YOU PLEASE SEND SOME AT ONCE. Forgetting the fact that you had no money, or assuming you had been wise enough to hang on to the cost of a cable, you would probably send something like: MONEY FINISHED PLEASE SEND MORE. You would only use the most important words in your message; you would have no room for explanations or qualifications. Adam's speech is much like that. It is very direct, consisting almost entirely of verbs and nouns.

Adam's mother, on the other hand, repeats and expands what Adam is saying to her. He says: 'There go one'; and she repeats that as 'Yes, there goes one.' In this way, she is teaching Adam.

Normally when people speak, they do not speak perfectly grammatically. Their grammar often gets confused in long sentences. They rely on the situation and the intonation to make their meaning clear. Yet, when she is speaking to Adam, Adam's mother speaks simply and with perfect grammar. The same seems to be true of most parents, or at least most middle-class parents, who have been studied. It is because they speak so correctly, sticking to all the rules, that their children manage

68

to pick up the incredibly intricate rules of language without being given any formal teaching.

In one experiment children were shown the following drawing.

They were told: This is a *wug*. They were then shown two of these creatures and asked to complete the sentence: Here are two ——. Most children of four and upwards replied *wugs*.

In a similar experiment, children were told that today Arthur was *glinging*. He did the same yesterday. The children were then asked to complete the sentence: Yesterday Arthur ——. Children from the age of four replied *glinged*. Adults, incidentally, are not sure if Arthur glinged, glang or glung.

The point of these studies is to show that very young children do pick up the basic rules of grammar without being aware of it. The four-year-old child is not going to be able to say that there is a rule that past tenses end in *-ed*. As children grow older they pick up the refinements of the language but the basics are there very early.

Considering the baby is born unable to speak a word, it is a tribute to the human brain that by the age of five most children are speaking in a way that is very close to the usual adult speech of their particular language.

This is such a phenomenal achievement that it seems likely that our brains are already programmed in some way to 're-ceive' language and respond to it. Otherwise, how could we learn to speak so well so quickly?

It is not just a question of automatic learning. Often parents talk *at* children, rewarding them with smiles, coos and praise when they babble and when they begin to speak. Look at a mother or a father – if you have the chance – when they see their eight-month-old baby babbling. You'll see a lot of very obvious rewarding. The baby gets all the attention with his babbling, just like a superb after-dinner speaker at a banquet.

What seems to clinch the idea that the brain is, in some way, genetically wired to respond to speech is that we could not learn to speak the way we do if each new brain were not specially prepared for hearing speech, developing it, and then turning out 'new speech of its own'. For we make sense of sentences that we have never heard before.

I have never written: 'I would be willing to take a bet that you've never seen this sentence before but that you will understand it.'

I understand it. Anyone can understand it. But we couldn't have learned and memorized it before since it is an original sentence. The wiring up within the brain seems to be very flexible, so that it can extract the patterns (both of grammar and of sense) that make up language. Children learn to understand sentences they have not heard before; they produce sentences they have not heard before; and children who are not taught or rewarded for learning how to speak appear to learn all the same. So there seems to be something innate in our brains that makes us speak and understand language. The odd thing is how many psychologists have been opposed to this view – that it is in the nature of man to speak.

Part of our brain has in it something like a computer programme. Much of it is wired up when we are born. The structure of this programme is such that it is ready to learn the rules of language merely by listening to language. As long as a child listens to language and as long as he does so before his brain reaches a certain stage of development, he will learn to speak. If, by the age of eight or ten perhaps, that has not happened, then the programme in the brain seems to wither.

Before that age, the capacity of children to make up for lost time can be remarkable. In the 1950s, a girl of $6\frac{1}{2}$ was found in Ohio, USA, living with her mother, who was a deaf mute. The child had been kept in the top part of a house and had never been spoken to. Two years after being found and placed in a more 'normal' environment, she spoke just like any other $8\frac{1}{2}$ year old.

But though the actual structure of the brain is important, it isn't everything. Learning to talk is a mixture of nature – what you inherit at birth – and nurture – what happens to you after you are born. Children whose parents talk to them and consciously try to develop their language tend to speak better; they use more complex sentences and a richer vocabulary. But unless a child is brought up in quite grotesque conditions, he or she will learn to speak pretty competently by the age of seven.

Just as birds are born with an instinct to fly, we are born with an instinct to talk. And that instinct depends on the make-up of our brain.

The way we speak also tells other people a great deal about us. Accents vary from region to region and from class to class. You still don't expect your doctor to have a ripe Cockney accent. If the fishmonger spoke with a plum in his mouth, you might wonder if he was putting it on.

Language isn't just a means of communication. It is also a means of division, especially in Britain. It tells people what your place in society is. We may suffer less from this than before, but we are still far from free of it.

The way we speak also reflects the things that bother us and that we have to cope with. Eskimos have no word for computer. My four-year-old son, who hasn't seen snow once in his life, can use the word *computer* pretty accurately. He says it's a machine that thinks. A four-year-old Eskimo child, on the other hand, would be well on the way to learning some of the fifty-odd words the Eskimos have for different kinds of snow. Such a wealth of snow-language would be wasted in south-east London.

GREAT AUTUMN MANOEUVRE

Hodge: 'Lor-a-massy, Me-aster! Be oi to be a "Power in t' Ste-ate"? What be oi to get by tha-at?'

Mr G: 'That, my good friend, is a mere detail. The question is, what am I to get by it!!'

"In the Debate as to giving a vote to the Agricultural Labourer, Mr Forster read a letter from the Premier, who declared that such extension of franchise was just and politic and could not *be avoided. The question was thus taken up by the government, which much needs a 'good cry'."*

★

Do you notice the difference in the way the poor man and his rich master talk? This cartoon was published when a new agricultural act gave the vote to agricultural labourers, even though some of them seem not to have wanted it.

From *The Cartoon History of England* by Michael Wynn Jones published by Tom Stacey.

And it's because language has to express new things that languages never stay the same. They grow. Old words die: new words come into being. In 1920, no one would have had a clue what a *raver* or a *groover* was. *Reggae* – what might that be? And if we know what all those mean, we don't know what it means to *gull* people (to con them) or to be a *varlet* – a cheeky young fellow.

Although some complain of the fact, language does change all the time. If we met a man from 1600, his accent would sound very strange and we would have difficulty in understanding him.

How We Behave When We Speak

So far, in this chapter, we've looked at language in isolation. But, of course, we do other things while we talk. Our mouths don't just open and shut.

One of the most fascinating pieces of recent psychological research has been to discover what we do while we are carrying on a conversation. For example, many of us have been taught to look someone straight in the eye when we talk to them, but almost no one does this for the whole of the time he's talking. Through a one-way mirror, psychologists observed where people looked while they talked. They found that a person's eyes would wander all over the place. Only when he stopped talking, and was signalling that it was time for his partner to start speaking, did he look him 'straight in the eye'. 'Over to you,' is the message that carries.

Psychologists found, moreover, that people are very skilful at timing the way they talk, almost like an orchestra. They pause often – to give the other person a chance to get in, or to look at him and see whether or not he has lost interest.

74

The team that has developed this way of examining how we behave when we talk also discovered that one of the things many psychiatric patients lacked was this kind of skill. They either stared at someone through most of the conversation or were so shy they looked away, or they interrupted constantly, never giving the other person the chance to speak. Not surprisingly, this kind of behaviour loses you friends and suggests that you need help.

As part of a general rehabilitation programme, psychologists are now teaching people how to behave when they speak. It sounds rather old-fashioned – classes in etiquette. But it isn't, of course. It is a question of training or re-training people who have lost what is a very basic set of skills that most of us never know we have. But we desperately need these skills if we are to communicate with each other.

If we did not talk, if we could not communicate with each other, we would be very different creatures. It is almost impossible to imagine what we would be like and what we could not do. But it is an interesting idea.

Touching Communication

You do not have to talk to someone to communicate with them. Gestures do nicely. Stick your tongue out, or wave a fist, and the person you are doing it to will get your meaning. But there are also rather more affectionate ways of saying something without speaking. You can touch people, give them a pat on the head, kiss them, give them a hug. Monkeys and apes are constantly touching each other. Human beings are more restrained but we also need to touch. There have even been extreme cases of babies who have died because they have hardly ever been touched.

75

We can touch and be touched on any part of our bodies From the tops of our heads to the tips of our toes, we are all skin. But, again, it is the brain that controls our sense of touch. The skin is full of little receptors. Some of these are more sensitive to pressure, some to temperature, some to pain. They send messages through the spine to the brain, which decodes them and works out what it is that we are feeling. Once the brain has decoded the message, it sends back – very fast if need be – instructions on what needs to be done then. For example, if you put your hand near a very hot plate, your skin has to detect that it feels too hot, and the brain, as soon as it gets that message, instructs your hand to pull itself away.

Information from the skin goes up to the brain through the spine. In the top part of the cortex there is a strip controlling our sense of touch and our movements that runs, very roughly, from one ear to the other. This is known as the motor strip and

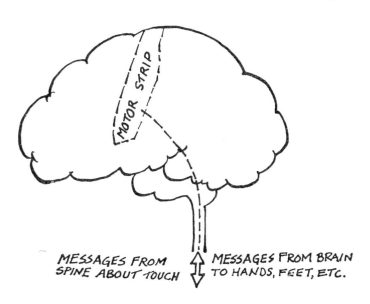

MESSAGES FROM SPINE ABOUT TOUCH   MESSAGES FROM BRAIN TO HANDS, FEET, ETC.

a good part of it controls the movements we make when we talk.

Because human beings rely so much on certain parts of the body, more space in the motor strip is devoted to these parts than to the less important ones. The number of cells that monitor our bottoms is not gigantic, for instance, however big the bottom. But our hands, our faces, our mouths need an extraordinary number of cells and a large area in the cortex,

The percentages refer to the area of the motor strip devoted to the particular part of the body.

because we do so much with them. With our hands we can do anything from punching to writing, to drawing, to tickling, to wielding a sledgehammer, to playing the most delicate note on a piano. With our mouths we eat, talk, breathe, kiss and, on occasion, spit. Such versatile organs require a lot of brain room.

Once in a while, people have been found who have no sense of touch or of pain. They are usually in terrible danger. Imagine what it would be like if your hand did not at once feel red hot when you put it on a hot plate on the stove. You might leave it there until, gruesome thought, it simply burnt off! Pain is a safeguard, though, of course, being in pain if you are ill is no joke. We feel pain because of the way in which the brain interprets the information coming to it from either the skin or the inside of the body. There isn't a pain centre in the brain, but when you feel something is wrong – too much pressure, too much heat – the body sends a rapid barrage of messages to the brain. Such a welter of information tells the brain that something is wrong and it acts to do what it can to get rid of the pain.

But we can be remarkably resilient to pain. It isn't just drugs that help, but a whole variety of things, including relaxing and just refusing to pay attention to the pain. Until recently, scientists have been baffled by this bizarre reaction. In the last few years, however, it has been discovered that there is a natural hormone substance which a certain area of the brain secretes and which seems to act as a powerful pain-killer. It's almost as if the brain had its own store of morphine, the strongest pain-killer. No one is quite sure yet how the brain manufactures this, or how it uses it. But it's an important discovery.

Touch, then, unlike our other senses, is the only sense that involves the whole body. We don't talk or hear or taste with our feet, or our hands, rumps or knees. But despite the fact that touch is all over the body, it is largely run from inside the head.

Do It Yourself

Ask someone to tickle you. Concentrate, if you can, on what you're feeling. Many people both like and hate being tickled because, at a certain point, you feel too much. Just as if the brain were being overwhelmed by too many, too strong, messages.

Hearing

There is no softest sound that the human ear can make out. What you hear depends on the circumstances and on the other noises around you. Sometimes you can hear a pin drop. Other times, you barely notice that someone has put on the radio as well as the television and the stereo – and the kettle's whistling as well!

In ideal conditions, the human ear is almost sensitive enough to hear the air vibrating around our bodies. We can count ourselves lucky our ears aren't quite so sharp. If they were, we would live in the midst of a constant buzz-buzz as the particles round our bodies collided, fused and split off. Could we then hear anything else?

And if that sounds remarkable, remember that human hearing is not all that sharp. If a cat or a dog were to wake up with human ears, he would think he had gone slightly deaf. Still, the loudest sound we can bear to hear is ten million million times as loud as the softest audible sound.

What are Sounds?

Sound is vibration. Sound waves are very much like the vibrations of a car or any other object. But sound vibrations can be of a much higher frequency than normal mechanical vibration. Different ears can catch different frequencies. The human ear can respond to frequencies between 20 and 20,000 cycles per second. A dog can hear higher pitched sounds – which is why someone who blows a dog whistle, which is pitched very high, hears nothing at all.

A sound first causes the air around it to compress and then to expand; this makes the sound waves. Sound waves travel at about 300 metres per second – you can get an idea of the time by going to a place where there are echoes and seeing how long it takes for the echo to boom back to you. Planes cross the sound barrier when they travel at over 1223 km per hour. As it travels, the sound wave peters out, and dies.

Because sound is created by vibrations, one can measure noise objectively. There is a scale in decibels from 0 to 140 – in other words, from silence to sound so loud that it would burst your ear-drum. A soft piece of music is 40 decibels: a lorry 90: Concorde taking off is 115 decibels. Decibels measure not the loudness you hear but the amount of vibration it takes to make a particular sound. The scale is logarithmic. One hundred decibels are not twice as loud as 50: 100 decibels are roughly 100,000 times as loud as 50. That means that to know how many decibels a particular sound makes does not tell you how loud it is. Loudness is subjective. If I like Mozart, I may have the hi-fi up very high and not think that it is that loud. If I hate the Rolling Stones, you may have them on very low – you know I don't like them and you're trying to be nice – but I may still think the Rolling Stones are very loud. Taste affects how loud we think things are.

It isn't just a matter of taste. Certain kinds of personality prefer loud noises. Extroverts may love the sound of jet engines, large bands and even factory machines; introverts are much less likely to. Since one is able to say how noisy a sound is in objective terms using decibels, one can then usefully compare other sounds. This makes laws forbidding certain noises as too loud a possibility.

A Picture of the Ear

The ear is a complicated device that analyses and begins to make sense of all these vibrations. Like the eye, the ear passes on messages in the form of biochemical reactions and electrical impulses. The sound that we know we hear is the result of much high speed analysis in the brain as well as in the ear.

The Ear within the Ear

What we think of as our ear is, to the anatomist, just the pinna, or flap, of the external ear. The pinna is nothing more than a decoration. It does none of our hearing. You can't even bend it this way and that in order to collect sounds better as the clever dog manages to do. South Sea islanders who hang jewels the size of soup plates from their ear lobes have learned the lesson that our outer ears are useless – although they are ticklish.

If the ear is not really the ear, then what do you hear with?

Our real ear is inside the ear. From the pinna, a small canal runs into the skull to the ear-drum, which marks the end of the outer ear. If you swim underwater without a bathing cap and water gurgles into your ears, it washes against the ear-drum and bounces out. The ear-drum is not, however, just there to protect, it also conducts sounds to the middle and inner ears, which is where we do our hearing.

Behind the ear-drum are the three bones of the middle ear and the canals that govern our sense of balance. The bones are set in an air-filled cavity which is connected by a tube to the mouth cavity. The sounds that hit the ear-drum are conducted

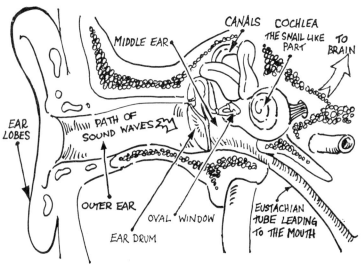

The ear.

across the three bones to the oval window of the inner ear.

From the oval window, we enter – so to speak – the inner ear. The part of the inner ear that is important for hearing is the cochlea. *Cochlea* means snail, and looks rather like a snail shell. It is a bony cavity shaped like a coil, in which there are three separate canals, divided from each other by two membranes, Reissner's membrane and the basilar membrane. Near the inner edge of the basilar membrane and towards the innermost part of the coil lies what is called the Organ of Corti, which contains hair cells.

Sound comes into the cochlea in the form of pressure. You can imagine it as a travelling bulge. This bulge moves through the canal of the cochlea, taking a different form depending on the actual frequency of sound that set it up. The canal in the cochlea is lined with tiny hairs, much like the hairs on the tongue.

THE ORGAN OF CORTI

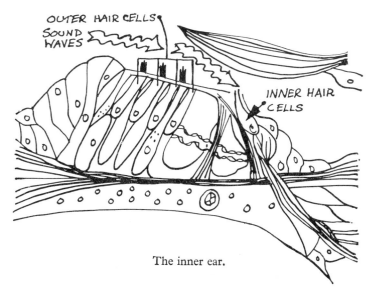

The inner ear.

Different hairs respond to different frequencies and strength of sound. As it travels up the canal of the cochlea, the bulge of pressure reaches a maximum point (which depends on the frequency and strength of sound). At this point 'its' hairs react most, and the energy of the sound, converted into pressure, is converted again into electrical and chemical impulses. These go to the nerves of the brain. The tiny hairs perform this quite stunning feat of turning mechanical pressure into electrical and chemical messages. Recordings have been made of the hair cells in the cochlea. They seem to act just like microphones, 'collecting' sounds, which they pass on inside the ear.

From the inner ear, the sound, coded into electrical and chemical messages, goes into the brain. Just as the eye performs the breakdown of light into messages, the ear breaks down sounds. We have two ears just as we have two eyes. And we use the minute difference between the time it takes for a sound to reach the left and the right ear to locate that sound.

Choosing to Hear

It is not enough, though, to understand what happens in our ears. We don't hear just with our ears.

Very often, our ears are bombarded with all kinds of different sounds. Imagine that you are in the living-room. The television is on. On the sofa, your uncle and your grandmother are having a conversation. There is a record on loud upstairs and, in the kitchen mother is trying to feed the baby, who is screaming. A noisy scene! A perfect microphone would pick up all these sounds and give them equal weight. If the brain were to do this, we would hear nothing but a confused buzz and noise. In fact, what the brain does is to filter out the noises that don't matter so that they don't bother us.

For example, if you are very interested in the television

programme in the noisy living-room, you will probably hear nothing but that; you will be largely unaware of the background noise. Your uncle and your grandmother, if they are absorbed in their conversation, are unlikely to hear much of what is going on on the television.

Some things immediately command our attention in such complex situations. For example, people will pick their own name more easily than anything else out of a general chaos of noise. Mothers will always hear a baby crying while they are sleeping though they may not 'hear' a train that passes at the bottom of their garden and makes just as much measurable noise. My elder son has never yet been woken by the screams of his younger brother, which make me jump out of the bed in another room. We hear what we listen for.

It is as if there were a kind of net in the brain. Some sounds always get through the net because they pass through holes: other noises may get through if they become loud enough.

The brain has to 'know' somehow which sounds are important enough for us to hear. It isn't a question of some organ, like the bones of the middle ear, acting as a filter; the way

sounds are analysed in the brain permits some form of pre-
liminary analysis so that, odd as it sounds, the brain can reject
those noises which there is no 'point' in our hearing. Sometimes, of course, we have become so used to a particular noise
that it is part of the background we don't hear. The famous
example of this is the man who has not heard the clock ticking
but hears that it has stopped ticking. The silence is noticeable.
If you can get access to a tape recorder – a cheap cassette is
ideal – you can get some idea of how selective the brain is in
the sounds it listens for.

Do It Yourself

Think of some friends of yours who will be willing to come and
listen to your tape. Try to find out the Christian names of their
parents too. Find a newspaper article that is not particularly
interesting. Read the article. You are going to record the article,
inserting the names of your friends and their parents in the
middle of sentences. Keep the microphone well away from you
as you record, speak low and, if you like, put the radio on. The
idea is to record a jumble of sounds mixed up with their names –
though, of course, you mustn't emphasize the names at all.

Now play the tape to your friends. See if they (i) hear their
names and (ii) how much else they hear. Psychologists would
predict that they would tend to hear their own name amongst
all the jumble.

A second, more complicated game is to record sentences, like
The man dumped over the fence or *The dog lit the cat*, in which
the verb is nonsensical though it rhymes with a verb that
would make perfectly good sense – the man jumped over the
fence. Now, play these confused sentences to your friends and
ask them what they heard.

Unless your friends are people with remarkable hearing, they will have heard *The man jumped over the fence* and *The dog bit the cat*. In other words, the brain tends to make sense of stuff it hears. If you have ever held a conversation on a very noisy telephone line, you will know how easy it is to guess what the other person is saying. That is the same kind of process.

Anyway, try it. Even if it fails totally – and experiments do sometimes fail totally for inexplicable reasons – you will have become very adept at using a tape recorder.

A lot of jokes depend on how easily we hear words wrong. Confusing our ears is a good way of getting a laugh. For example:

> What did the coke say to the coal?
> What kind of fuel am I?

> Knock, knock.
> Who's there?
> Luke.
> Luke who?
> Luke through the keyhole and you'll see.

Author's note: these are not my jokes.

Learning to Hear

In the chapter on vision, I pointed out that we are not born seeing. We have to learn to see. You might expect, therefore, the baby to be born a little deaf, too. Cooped up in the womb, what can it have heard?

In fact, the foetus lying inside its mother is exposed to constant sounds. Usually the ears are formed partially at 12 weeks. At 6 months, they look like, and work like, ears. And while the eyes can get no practice in the womb, the ears get plenty of sounds. To begin with there are the sounds the mother's body makes. A film called *The Body* pioneered the technique of getting a person to swallow a minute camera and tape recorder. The workings of the body are noisy indeed. Moreover, the baby in the womb has plenty that it can hear going on outside its mother, for skin does not offer much resistance to sound.

There is no simple way to test this. If you have a mother or a friend or a relative who is pregnant, you can ask her if she knows whether the baby hears. Mothers often remember that a particularly loud noise startled the child in the womb because they could feel it tense up or kick. Sometimes music may make the baby 'dance' in the womb. Because of this, when the baby is born, he or she has already got ears that work perfectly well.

In fact, a baby who is only five weeks old will usually turn his head in the direction of a sound. This means that he can localize sounds with almost no experience of hearing in the outside world.

Do It Yourself

1. Which of the following kinds of music do you like: folk songs; heavy rock; soft smoochy music; loud hymns; brass bands; someone humming?

2. Which of the following sounds do you like: crowds chanting; bird song; fast cars revving; a watch ticking; airplanes taking off?

3. Now make a list of three other noises that you particularly like.

When you have done all that, look to see if most of the noises you like are soft or loud. If they are soft, it suggests you are a little bit frightened of being too excited. If they are loud, it means that you like a good deal of very obvious excitement and are something of an extrovert.

Now if you like soft noises, go somewhere quiet and yell for ten seconds just to see what it feels like: if you like loud noises, go somewhere quiet and whisper just to see what that feels like.

Sound is a Pleasure

Obviously, animals have to hear in order to survive. To be able to tell that your enemy might be approaching from the left, because you hear ominous noises, is essential for staying alive in the jungle. It still is now. How difficult it must be for a deaf person to cross a busy street at a corner! Animals that hunt, as did our ancestors, also rely on their hearing to tell them where to find their prey. Man relies more on his sight, which is especially good at picking out movement. Once our ancestors wanted to communicate with each other, much the easiest way was by making sounds that came to have some meaning. Why we have hearing is obvious.

What is much less obvious is why certain kinds of sounds –

especially certain patterns and rhythms of sounds such as you find in music – should give us so much pleasure.

Why Does Music Sound Nice?

It may sound an odd question, but is it? Why should we enjoy a certain pattern of sounds? It's clear that almost all peoples have some kind of music. Even 'primitive' Indian tribes near the tip of South America have flute-like instruments on which they play reedy, haunting melodies. Why?

The answers we can give at present are a bit vague. We enjoy listening to sounds that are familiar and to sounds that are new. Good music mixes them. Listen carefully to a particular piece of music that you like and see if you think to yourself: 'Ah . . . there's that bit I like again.' When you know a piece of music, you anticipate the return of a particular sequence of notes. At the same time, music that is completely predictable tends to be boring. We like the shock effect of a sudden loud section, a sudden silence or an unexpected soft piece.

These elements play a part in making us love or hate a

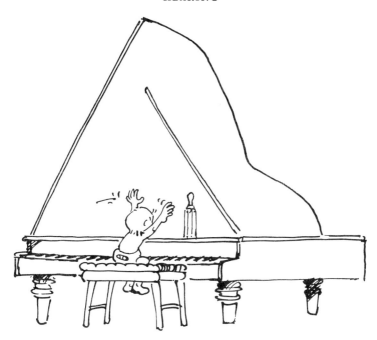

particular piece of music but it is not clear exactly how. The brain has its own rhythms and so it has been suggested that we may like certain rhythms because these go in time with our natural brain rhythms. It's an intriguing thought but it hasn't been proved to date.

Musical ability often develops young and runs in families. The great composer, J. S. Bach, had four sons and a grandson who were composers – several of them very famous. Mozart's father was a professional musician and Mozart was a concert pianist by the age of four. Recently, a Japanese music teacher, Suzuki, has started to teach children to play the violin as soon as they can walk. Suzuki argues that a child's mind is very receptive to musical experiences when he or she is two to three years old; if you begin to teach music then, it is very easy for him to pick it up and to develop whatever musical talents he may have. To prove Suzuki's point, many of his pupils have become internationally recognized musicians in their teens and early twenties.

This fact that it is so easy to teach young children confirms the fact that the young brain is very sensitive to experiences. And it suggests that perhaps children could learn to do many things much earlier than adults normally imagine they can.

Sound is Stress

Sounds can give pleasure but they can also give pain. The human ear is only designed to cope with a certain amount of noise. If our ears have to hear louder noise, they suffer. The Department of Employment in Britain warns factory owners not to let people be exposed to noise above the limits shown opposite.

Under no circumstances should any one ever listen to a single noise of 115 decibels without having their ears protected. And, the Department points out, ordinary ear plugs or sticking a bit of cotton wool in your ears is not good enough.

Beyond the limits indicated, your hearing will suffer because your inner ear will be worn down and over-strained. It is not quite like looking straight at the sun – which the eyes cannot cope with – but it is still overloading, giving the ears more than they were ever meant to take.

It isn't just factory workers who face the risk of losing their hearing. People living just by motorways often complain of the noise pollution. A number of scientists have looked at the hearing of pop musicians who use a great deal of amplification. The results aren't comforting. Discos often had noise at over 110 decibels – above danger level. Most of the pop musicians

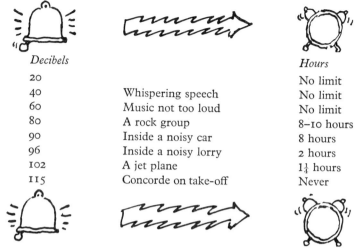

Decibels		Hours
20		No limit
40	Whispering speech	No limit
60	Music not too loud	No limit
80	A rock group	8–10 hours
90	Inside a noisy car	8 hours
96	Inside a noisy lorry	2 hours
102	A jet plane	$1\frac{1}{4}$ hours
115	Concorde on take-off	Never

had lost about 3 per cent of their hearing capacity; they had in particular lost the ability to hear certain speech frequencies well. Those who listened to pop concerts had suffered much the same fate. With so much decay of the ears, we can look forward to rather deaf pop bands playing amazingly loud music to

rather deaf pop fans who will have to try really hard to hear at all. What a lovely prospect! What fine music we shall have!

Since the noise Concorde makes at take-off is around 115 decibels and the noise of a conventional jet around 102, the levels of noise people are allowed by law to make are very high. Perhaps they ought to be reduced. There is evidence that people are going deaf because they have to cope with too much noise.

Noises You Like

At the start of this chapter, I tried to point out that decibels were an objective measure of noise because they measured how much sound energy it took to create a particular noise. Noise and loudness are two different things.

For example some subjects have actually enjoyed listening to the noise that Concorde makes! Other people – less desperate for having their ears blown out – still like a background of noise. I know people who like having the radio on even though they hardly listen to it. It makes a kind of wall-paper of sound. Other people prefer silence to be silent.

Precisely because how much noise you like is a matter of personal choice, we need an impersonal scale by which to measure noise. If you are going to prevent cars and airplanes making too much noise – as many recent laws have – then there has to be a standard of noisiness. Decibels give this.

Before it reaches the point of damaging our ears, noise can affect the way that we do things! In the past, we lived in a very quiet world; thunder must have been the loudest noise early humans had to suffer. I expect people who live near London Airport and who have to put up with lots of planes would much prefer the occasional thunderstorm even if they had to have the weather that went with it. Thunder is much softer than a

As time goes on, sounds get louder and louder.

jet-engine – at least from the ground. Today we live in a very noisy world.

It has been found that in noisy conditions people work much less efficiently and tend to suffer from stress. They get ill more often and they are absent from work for no good reason. A recent study also found that people help each other much less in such an environment. Our ears were never designed to cope with such a general loud level of noise – and we suffer when we have to try and do it, as many of us do now.

The ironical thing is that while too much noise is bad for you, a little noise – of the right kind – can help. Since the War, a special kind of music, called Muzak, has been developed; you can hear its bland tones in plenty of shops, restaurants and airports. Muzak is music with all the bumps smoothed out electronically. It has no great changes of rhythm or tune or pitch, and drones pleasantly on. Because it is so bland, Muzak

asks nothing of the brain while helping to keep it alert. It even helps cows to produce more milk and hens to lay more eggs, according to some scientists. Factories and offices are also said to work better when this kind of faceless music is played. The reason, apparently, is that Muzak 'tones' up the brain and is just loud enough to mask sounds that might be distracting.

Do It Yourself

Make a tape of the following noises – a car engine revving up, breathing, stones rattling inside a tin can, screaming, a soft Frank Sinatra record and a rock number like 'Leader of the Gang'. Play these tapes to some of your friends and ask them to rank them (i) in order of loudness – from loudest to softest – and (ii) in order of preference, from 1 to 6.

See if there is any connection between the two . . .

A very practical thing you can do is to try and borrow a decibel-meter. (Your school, if it has not got one, will probably be able to borrow one from the public health department of the local council or from the Noise Abatement Society, 6 Old Bond Street, London w1.)

Go with some friends to a busy road and register the noise levels that passing traffic makes. Then ask passers-by if they found the noise of the lorry or the car that has just gone by loud, very loud, not that loud, quiet or very quiet. Compare their answers with the readings you get from the meter.

The Evolving Ear . . .

We use our noses much less than we must have done once. We may not use our ears more but they certainly have to cope with levels of sound that are quite new. Can you imagine ways in which the ear will evolve to deal with that? It is an intriguing thought that, in the future, our ears may have to become somewhat different if the world we live in continues to get noisier and noisier.

The Way you React

The Way We Look

On this page there are four faces. Each face seems to be in a very different kind of mood, feeling a different kind of feeling. Can you tell what each of them is feeling?

If you think you can, write down the feeling that 'goes' with each face on a piece of paper.

When you have finished, put the piece of paper away. Then go and stand in front of a mirror. Take a good look at your face. (I'm sorry if it sounds absurd and complicated but there really is a point to it.)

Now that you are in front of the mirror (if you've agreed to play this game), try to look very sad – and then try to look very happy. The thing that you will probably realize is that in putting on both faces the parts of the face that you use most are the eyes and the mouth. They are the parts that are most mobile and, also, most expressive. If you are sad, your eyes are turned down and your mouth droops. On this page you will see some sketches of faces that really show nothing but the shape of the face and the position of the eyes and mouth: they are almost as expressive as photographs.

Do you feel hesitant about saying what expression each of these faces conveys? If so, you are in a minority. Most of us are sure we read faces like these pretty well.

We seem to learn quite young to recognize that different expressions mean different feelings. A three-year-old child is quite capable of saying: 'Why do you look so sad, mum?' even though mum has not breathed a word about feeling sad. The older we grow, the more sure we become of this skill. We use it in everyday life. Next time someone walks into the room, try to guess his mood from the way he looks. You probably have been doing it for years anyway.

Charles Darwin (1809–82) showed a number of photographs of faces, which, he thought, clearly demonstrated certain emotions, to twenty people. They agreed on some of the photographs but, on others, they could not agree at all which emotion the face expressed. This puzzled Darwin. Many psychologists have repeated this kind of experiment. The first interesting thing is that very few people feel that they cannot *read off*, as it were, a person's emotion from a still photograph. We assume we can do it. The second interesting thing is that a number of studies reveal the fact that there are six main kinds of emotional expression that we can see in faces. These are:

1. Love, happiness and mirth.
2. Surprise.
3. Fear and suffering.
4. Anger and determination.
5. Disgust.
6. Contempt.

By and large, people are very good at reading the expression. In some studies, actors were asked to put on a whole gamut of emotional expressions and people could, more or less, guess them right. But there is one problem.

There is little likelihood that you will mistake someone who looks disgusted for someone who looks in love. But it is quite easy for someone to see an expression of *fear* as one of *anger*, or one of *disgust* as one of *contempt*. Given this list, it is easy that people make a mistake of one step. They don't confuse 1 and 4 or 1 and 3 but it is very possible to mistake 3 and 4.

Imagine – to be very dramatic – that you have walked into a room where someone has just died. The faces look very intense.

You do not see the dead man; you cannot hear what they are saying. Would you be able to tell whether they were angry (4) or suffering (3)? Possibly not. In real life, of course, our task is made much easier by the fact that we know much more about what is going on. If you hear someone scream: 'I'll get the bastards who did it,' you can safely bet not just that he is feeling more than sad, but also that he is very angry. If no one is saying anything and you see that a man has obviously just died, you will have little trouble in realizing that people are feeling very sad. Faces tell us a lot about what it is that people feel but they don't tell us everything. They don't have to, since, outside experiments in a psychology lab, you don't see faces in isolation. They are always in the middle of some situation.

Brain and Mood

The brain both affects and reflects our moods. When you are very happy or very depressed there will be subtle changes in the brain. Psychiatric patients who suffer from clinical depression or from abrupt changes in mood often have either a slight excess or a slight lack of various biochemical substances in their brains. This is not to say that they are depressed *because* they have too much chemical X. In fact, it is known that many quite unchemical factors contribute to depression, like bad housing, having a bad marriage, being out of work or having a job that one finds too difficult. But there is a relationship between our mood and the biochemical state of our brain.

The most obvious example of this is alcohol. When adults drink a little they often function better. They tend to be a bit more relaxed. But if they drink more than a little, the balance changes. The brain cannot cope with so much alcohol and it has to use oxygen in order to burn it up. That deprives other areas of much-needed oxygen and they are not able to work as well as they might. Certain biochemicals, too, like noradrenalin, make one feel very emotional so that it is easy either to start laughing at the most pathetic jokes or to get angry without due provocation. In other words, the brain's chemistry can be altered and that can alter our mood. The opposite is also true. If you feel ecstatic, and you could get a complete read-out of your brain's state, you would find it was quite different from the state it was in before your ecstasy.

Pretending

People can do another thing that, it seems fair to assume, animals cannot do. They can pretend. Anyone who is good at pretending learns how to use his face, his voice and what he is saying to convey an impression. He is putting on a show of giving people all the messages that say 'I'm sad' while, inside, he may be giggling at the success he's having.

Children learn quite slowly and clumsily that they can do this. It is a very sophisticated business. To bring it off, you have to be able to do a number of things. You must know enough about yourself to know that you are not sad. You must know enough about how you, and other people, behave when they are sad to be aware of what you have to do in order to convince others that you are sad. And you have to be able to execute it, to act it out.

There have been very few studies of how well – and at what age – children can pretend certain things. They seem to learn to pretend first of all by pretending to be things. It is easier to pretend to be an elephant than it is to pretend to be sad, because you just have to bellow and stomp around – preferably explaining to others that you are being an elephant! No human can really be much like an elephant, so the show can be pretty crude. But we all know exactly what you should look like if you are feeling sad. We are much sharper judges of that. The performance has to be better. And a child takes a great deal of time to be able to put that together. By the age of four, however, most children seem to be able to mimic emotions well enough to pretend they are feeling something they are not *without* fooling their parents. And by the age of eight most children have managed to reach the delightful stage of doing it well enough to fool their parents – at least some of the time.

Those adults who are particularly good at deceiving people develop one very clever trick. In the chapter on talk we saw that most people look away for much of the time they are talking to you. The 'deceivers' look straight into people's eyes. When I was a child, my parents spent a great deal of time telling me that I must look people straight in the eye when talking to them, because this is usually taken as a mark of honesty: shifty eyes have something to hide. For the unpractised deceiver that may be so, but the really accomplished deceiver is the man who can lie and look you in the eye more than most.

Do It Yourself

With a friend practise having a conversation in which (i) you never stop looking each other in the eye, and (ii) you never look each other in the eye at all. Describe – and get your friend to describe – the way you feel on both occasions.

You and Your Temperament

Just as we seem to enjoy the business of working out how someone feels from the way they look, we also seem to need to try and work out what people are like. Listen to people talking.

Very often, they talk about other people. In fact, if we didn't have other people to praise, bitch about and mull over, the art of human conversation would be almost dead. A good deal of the discussion revolves round the topic of what other people are like. We say things like: 'Isn't Fred a happy man,' or 'Typical of Sue to be so bad tempered.' And we expect people to be consistent. If we come across usually cheerful Fred looking wet with tears, we wonder what it is that has made him feel so unlike himself. Many plays and books are based on the principle that the hero or heroine is meek, sweet and has no confidence. A series of dreadful ordeals are placed in his or her way. In the end, ordeals are overcome and, presto, the person's character changes. Psychiatrists have even taken to using this as a means of curing people who are depressed. They argue that people are depressed because most of the things that happen to them are depressing. Every time they try to do something, they fail. Their boss bawls them out; their teacher snarls at them. Instead of tampering with the depressed person, this new kind of therapy tampers with their environment. The psychiatrist allows himself to lose arguments with him. The teacher is contacted and asked not to snarl at the child but, the next time the chance arises, either to praise him or, if possible, to lose an argument to him. This form of therapy has been tried with adults and the results are claimed to be good. People tend to become less depressed as they see themselves being less helpless.

The point that this shows up is that we learn what we are like not only by ourselves but by the way people act towards us. In one experiment, a girl who was neither particularly bright nor particularly attractive was undergoing treatment. Her teacher, and everyone in her class, was asked to act towards her as if she were very bright and very attractive. Boys asked her out. Teachers gave her good marks. At the beginning of the year, she believed that she was neither very bright nor very attractive. She had a fairly accurate idea of herself. By the end of the year, she believed herself to be much brighter and much more attractive. One key part of her experience, how people behaved towards her, had changed. And that was enough to change her. (The psychologists did not, alas, press on with the study and say what happened after the year was out).

Imagine a small child who is always treated by his parents as if he were stupid. His parents do not talk to him much, except to scold him. Everything he or she does is wrong. If he does something well, they ignore it. They never praise him. Would it be surprising if such a child came to feel that he was a failure? He may be lucky and meet teachers and friends who give him a very different idea of himself, but then they will be impressing a new picture of what he is like on to him. Would it work?

The older one gets, the more able one becomes in discovering what one feels about oneself from what others feel and think about you. But, by that time, enough people have contributed to making you feel about yourself whatever it is that you feel.

More than we like to admit, we are what others make us.

Adults certainly come to see themselves very much as others see them. Asked to give twenty replies to the question 'What am I', most American people described themselves in terms of their job and status. I am a doctor. I am a house-owner. I am married. I am a car owner. I am a father. Far fewer answers talked about people's feelings and thoughts and ambitions yet you might think if you gave someone the chance to answer such a deeply personal question as 'What am I' (and they agreed) that they would see themselves in a more personal way. But the first things that people define themselves by are precisely those things that other people use to define them. Think of Jones and the first thought you have is that, indeed, he is a doctor or a mechanic or whatever. That may be particularly American, and it may be changing, but it is odd.

Different Kinds of Personality

The Greeks believed that people had one of four different temperaments – the fiery, the airy, the watery or the earthy. Fiery people were passionate, quick to anger, confident and not that reliable. Earthy people were much slower, more practical and more reliable. Airy people were dreamers, out of touch with the ordinary ruck of events. Watery people were placid, sluggish and not easily excited or perturbed. Each type was supposed to be linked to a particular physical build.

In fact, the idea that fat men are jolly or that thin men are mean and suspicious is deeply rooted. In Shakespeare's *Julius Caesar*, the about-to-be-assassinated Caesar says of Cassius, one of the conspirators:

> Yond Cassius has a lean and hungry look;
> He thinks too much: such men are dangerous. (I. ii. 193–4)

Some psychologists have believed that the shape of our body is linked with our personality. We certainly have typical images like the jolly fat man, the lean tortured intellectual. The illustrations on page 112 are of very extreme types. Usually, people are a mixture – tending towards leanness or towards stockiness. Psychologists have developed very precise ways of measuring the kind of body-type you are. And some psychologists think that this influences the sort of person you are. Criminals were once supposed to have particular shapes, a quite false idea!

But though some psychologists argue that this is true, others dismiss it as nonsense. The problem with personality is that psychologists disagree almost totally about it. They disagree on what forms a person's personality: some claim it is the heredity one is born with; others say that it is what happens during the first five years of life that determines personality; others argue that people learn to play different roles in different situations and don't really have a distinct personality. The result is confusion, argument and debate.

An interesting theory – and that, of course, doesn't mean that it is true – is that there are certain very important features which make up a person's character. These can be measured by getting people to fill in tests such as this one:

1. Are you often in a bad mood for no reason?
2. Do you like going to parties?

3. Do you enjoy the company of other people?
4. Do you find practical jokes a bit silly?
5. Do you get angry very easily?
6. Do you often find that you are brooding by yourself?
7. Do you like crowds?
8. Do you find it hard to talk to your parents' friends?
9. Do you sweat a lot?
10. Are you good at thinking on your feet?
11. Would you prefer to spend the afternoon reading a book you love rather than go out with your friends?
12. Do you cry easily in public?

If you have done the test, you have just completed part of what is known as a Personality Inventory, which aims to test whether you are an introverted or extroverted personality. If you answered 'yes' to 2, 3, 5, 7, 10 and 12, you are extroverted; if you answered 'yes' to 1, 4, 6, 8, 9 and 11, you are introverted.

So what?

The point about this theory of personality is that it argues that you are likely to behave in a certain way if you are introverted and in a different way if you are extroverted. Take, for example, a man who is extroverted. He is likely to have a good sense of humour, to work at his best during the afternoon and to enjoy seeing a lot of different things during the day. The more stimulation he gets the better. He feels confident and relaxed when dealing with people. He is likely to go in for quite different jobs from an introvert – politics, salesmanship, acting or teaching. On the other hand, he is likely to talk too much, to be quite superficial in his relationships and to concentrate less well than an introvert on doing long tasks. An introvert responds better to praise when doing a job, the extrovert to criticism. By making the extrovert feel guilty or bad, you might get him to make the effort to concentrate.

THE JOLLY FAT MAN

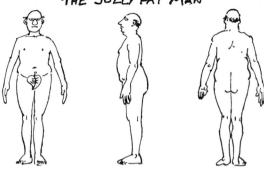

LEAN TORTURED INTELLECTUAL

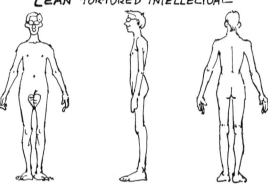

AVERAGE MAN OF ACTION

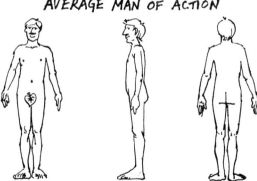

Different body types.

These are only some of the things that extroverts are likely to do and to feel. But it begins to build up a picture of a person's character.

No one is completely extrovert or completely introvert. We are all some of both. We each have, however, more of one tendency than the other. According to the theory, you can measure precisely by doing tests like this how extroverted, introverted or neurotic you are. And by knowing the extent of each trait, you should be able to predict how you are likely to act in various situations.

The trouble with this theory is that it is so very limited. Those who hold it agree that other traits ought to be found

which would explain personality in a more complex, realistic way. But there are psychologists who think that every person is unique, and to some extent this is true: no theory can explain away those qualities, attitudes, feelings and ideas that are unique to one person. To try to be scientific about personalities in the way that people are scientific about gravity and how you make gas seems to some psychologists quite misguided.

In other words, it's a field where there is more debate and discussion than actual facts that everybody accepts. So, by all means, do the test on page 110 and guess what kind of temperament you have, but don't accept it as a sacred truth.

Do It Yourself

On a piece of paper, write a few lines about the scenes that are portrayed in pictures A and B. Explain why the children are doing what they're doing.

Probably, you will have written a story that does not describe

what is going on but, in some way, tries to explain why it is that the little boy is crying or the girl is looking so serious as she tries to read. Just as we learn to read faces, we learn, as we grow up, that people don't do things for no reason at all. We try to explain why we do things.

The Flying Pigeon

During the Second World War, the American armed forces worked on a primitive missile. They had no sophisticated equipment to guide this missile, but planned, instead, to use pigeons strapped into the front of the missile to keep it on course. This remarkable idea was the work of an American psychologist, Burrhus Skinner.

Skinner believed one could train pigeons to do the job. Inside the nose-cone of the missile was a metal disc with a cross on it. The cross had to be in the dead centre for the missile to be on target: if it moved, the missile was 'off'. By pecking at the metal disc it was possible to get the cross back in the centre, and this would, in turn, affect the steering mechanism. Skinner had to train pigeons so that they would be motivated to go on pecking the metal disc for hours without getting an immediate reward.

What Skinner did first was to get the pigeons used to the task. This was no particular problem. They would start by getting a reward – a pellet of food – every time they pecked. Then, slowly, it was every tenth time they pecked; then every fiftieth time; then every hundredth time. By the end of their training, they had been trained to accept as a sufficient reward a pellet of food every thousandth time or so that they pecked. In other words, strapped into their flying missile, they would

MISSILE ON COURSE

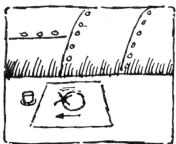

MISSILE OFF COURSE
PIGEON IS TRAINED TO
PECK WHEN 'X' IS OUT
OF CIRCLE

PIGEON PECKS MISSILE
BACK ON COURSE

keep on pecking indefinitely at the metal disc, making sure that the cross was in the centre till the missile hit its target – when they would get a reward they certainly did *not* expect.

In the end, this ingenious device never flew. The military decided the missile was not necessary, but it had proved to be quite successful in tests.

People are not pigeons. But much of the knowledge we have about why people do things comes from studies of animals. There is a long tradition of research that treats humans almost as though they were pigeons.

People have certain basic needs. If I am hungry I need to eat. If I am tired I need to sleep. If I am thirsty I need to drink. Most people also have a drive to have sex. There are other more complicated needs, which we will come to. In the fairly rich countries of the West, most people have food, drink and shelter available, and so we eat when hungry, drink when thirsty, sleep when tired. We can say that hunger makes us eat, thirst makes us drink and tiredness makes us sleep. But saying that really does not tell us very much. What scientists have done, therefore, is to try and find out what it is that the body's tissues are lacking when we feel hungry or thirsty or sleepy. They have identified a series of biochemical states, and claim that it is because our body tissues lack certain substances and are in such and such a biochemical state, that we feel hungry. Then hunger will make us eat and the food will give the body the resources it is in need of.

Animals that have been deprived of food will certainly learn a task like finding their way through a very simple maze much more quickly if there is a food reward at the end of it. The same goes for thirst. If a rat needs to mate and at the end of the maze he will find a mate, he learns to negotiate that maze more quickly.

People have assumed that you can treat people in pretty much the same way. To a degree, it makes sense. Why do people work? Part of the answer is that by working they earn money and money enables them to buy food, drink and shelter for themselves and their families. Many people do dull jobs that they dislike throughout their lives. Their only reason for doing so is that they need to earn the money to satisfy these and other needs. And if people are in a situation where they are without food, drink or shelter, they will go to extraordinary lengths to get it.

Take an extreme case. We have been brought up to think of cannibalism as disgusting. I can't even begin to think of eating another person without feeling sick though I tuck into beef and lamb and pork with much delight. Many people think that eating meat is wrong anyway so one can imagine how horrible the idea of eating a fellow human being is.

But there have been two cases in the past five years of people doing just that. In both cases, they were pushed to do it by circumstances, by the sheer instinct to survive. In one case, a pilot crashed over the Canadian forests and was not rescued for about three weeks. His companion – a nurse – had died in the crash. To survive, he ate parts of her.

An even more famous case is that of the air crash in the Andes which was the subject of a book, *Alive*, by the novelist Piers Paul Read. Here some of the party survived the crash. High up in the mountains, there was nothing to eat but human flesh. In the end, hunger made them eat it even though, as religious men, they were full of qualms.

In neither case was it a story of vicious men or women getting their teeth into human flesh. The people were all honourable and pained. They said that they saw no point in dying of starvation. And though none of them enjoyed the actual taste or the process of eating, they did it – driven by hunger.

What was especially interesting about their reactions was that they did not feel terribly guilty about what they had done.

But human beings don't do things just because they need to eat, drink, sleep and have sex.

Children certainly seem to feel a need to explore everything about them. A small baby will not lie around still and bored if he or she is not being fed. As soon as he can move his arms and open his eyes, he will start looking around. Once he is able to get hold of things, he will begin to grab at everything. When a

baby reaches six months or nine months, he will spend some of his time crawling around and exploring, which usually means grabbing objects and trying to eat them. But the baby is not really hungry. What he is motivated to do is to search out the world around him and, as far as possible, make sense of it. Rats do the same. If you put a rat in an interesting colourful maze, it will explore it quite thoroughly, even though it is getting no reward.

Human history would have been very different if we had not been seized with the urge to explore both the world and how the world works. If you discover America like Christopher Columbus, it is true that you are likely to become rich; if you manage to climb Everest, it is true that you are likely to become famous. But few people who read the biographies of explorers believe they were willing to face dangers just out of greed. And people who 'explored' in the sense of finding out about things rarely did it for money or fame alone. They very often had a driving need to find out about something or to prove something.

This need to explore things and find out about them seems to be linked with a need we have to feel in control of things. No one likes to feel helpless.

We also have other needs that motivate us. We need friendship. We need affection. We need to feel we are achieving something. We will all do a lot to satisfy these needs.

For a long time, psychologists believed we were driven mainly by sexual energy. The theory was as follows. Since we cannot spend all our time having sex – for then the world would simply stop functioning – society evolved ways of training children to be less sexual. This meant that there was an overspill of sexual energy, which was used to 'fuel' us to do other things. The athlete ran, the factory worker laboured, the secretary typed, the businessman haggled, all on energy which was really sexual but which could not be expressed sexually. So that a sportsman would use sport in order to get rid of his sexual energy.

It now seems clear that the reasons why we do all the various things we do are much more complicated. If our basic needs for food, water and shelter are not satisfied, we will go to extremes to satisfy them, but that does not explain most of our actions most of the time. We have a whole set of social needs – for friendship, affection, conversation – as well. We also have a set of personal needs. It is the fact that each of us is separate and unique that makes trouble for psychologists – trouble some of them have not been willing to face up to.

An apple is essentially like another apple. If you can explain why one apple falls to the ground, you can assume that will hold good for all other apples. If you explain the chemical make-up of one piece of lead, that will hold good for other pieces of lead. People are simply more individual.

Individuality comes out in the complex reasons each of us has for wanting to do certain things and for feeling or thinking certain ideas. Take two brothers who have been brought up in the same home by parents equally devoted to them both. Why does one brother, in his last year at school, decide that he is going to work in his spare time so that he can afford to spend the next summer travelling round Europe, while the other brother does next to nothing? But the energetic brother is rather shy of people and will not go out of his way to make friends or chat up girls, while the can't-be-bothered brother spends much of his time simply talking with other people. One brother hopes to become a successful doctor: the other doesn't care what he is going to do. Even these details, which are fairly superficial, suggest how impossible it is to argue that we all will be very much alike if we come from the same background. Two people

can also do exactly the same thing for quite different reasons. Mark may swot because he really wants to pass his exams; Fred may swot because his parents will be angry if he does badly; Joanna may be bribed. If she gets through the exam, they will take her for a week-end in Paris. People's motives remain very individual, which makes it hard for psychologists to crack them.

Do It Yourself

Choose one or two of your friends. Try to remember something that you did recently together. Write down the reasons why each of you did it and what each of you (i) enjoyed and (ii) hated about it.

When you have finished that, write down what it is that is likely to make you do things; also write down whether you would rather devote yourself to doing something easy that you know you can pull off or something difficult at which you may fail.

Compare your answers.

In this chapter I have sketched out some of the motives we have for doing things. To sketch out all of them would take much longer and would involve examining the idea that we often do things for reasons that we are not aware of. For instance, if you keep on 'forgetting' to meet your friend it may not be that you have a bad memory (which is what you blame it on since you tell yourself you want to see her) but that you really don't want to see her – but can't actually let yourself know that that is how you feel about it. People's motives can be unconscious. That is one whole field I have not gone into. I have to repeat that the subjects of personality and motivation are much more controversial among scientists than the question of how we see, hear, smell, taste or learn to talk. The reason is that many of the ideas psychologists had about them have turned out to be wrong – you cannot even explain the way a rat behaves by assuming food, thirst, sex and sleep and the need to urinate and defecate are the sum total of its reasons for doing anything. And a person is far more complicated than a rat. Because of the complexity of personality and motivation, psychologists are very far indeed from putting together convincing theories about them. This has to remain a chapter full of question marks – which is no bad thing, since that is very much the state of psychology today.